17a

IS
mca.Traw
ash

THE PRESERVATION OF TIMBER

THE PRESERVATION OF TIMBER

BY

W. P. K. FINDLAY

D.SC., A.I.C.T.A., D.I.C., F.I.W.SC.

WITH 30 PHOTOGRAPHS
AND 6 DRAWINGS

ADAM & CHARLES BLACK
LONDON

FIRST PUBLISHED 1962
BY A. AND C. BLACK LTD.
4, 5 AND 6 SOHO SQUARE, LONDON W.I

To My Wife

*with grateful appreciation of her help
in the preparation of the manuscript*

PRINTED IN GREAT BRITAIN BY
ROBERT CUNNINGHAM AND SONS LTD., ALVA

CONTENTS

v

ILLUSTRATIONS

PREFACE

ALTHOUGH the wood preserving industry was established well over a hundred years ago in this country no text-books on the subject of timber preservation have been written in Great Britain. The standard works which do already exist either relate to American conditions or else they are written in a foreign language. There seemed therefore to be a need for a book that would bring together much of the technical information that has been published in bulletins and leaflets by the Forest Products Research Laboratory, the British Wood Preserving Association and many industrial firms. Architects, builders, landowners and farmers are sometimes bewildered by the choice of preservatives offered by the manufacturers, and this book has been written with a view to helping them to choose the most suitable product for their particular purpose and to use it to the best advantage. It is not intended as a manual for plant operators, but rather as a guide for all users of timber and timber products.

ACKNOWLEDGEMENTS

I AM indebted to the Director of the Forest Products Research Laboratory for permission to reproduce those photographs marked 'Crown Copyright'. I am grateful to the firms who so kindly supplied the information contained in the Appendix on proprietary wood preservatives and to Mr W. E. Bruce of the British Wood Preserving Association for his advice.

For the loan of the undermentioned photographs grateful thanks are due to:

Plates

II, 6, 7; XII, 1, 2. Mr D. Boocock, Preservation Developments Ltd.

VI, 2. Mr E. H. B. Boulton, Pestcure Ltd.

III, 1, 2, 4. Celcure Ltd.

III, 5, 6, 7. Cobra Wood Treatments, Ltd.

III, 8. Hicksons Timber Impregnation Co.

III, 3. also Text Figs. 1, 2, 3, 4, Pratchitt Bros.

VI, 1. Mr S. A. Richardson, Messrs Richardson and Starling.

INTRODUCTION

THE total financial loss due to the premature decay of wooden structures through various kinds of rot and insect attack amounts every year to a formidable sum. A great deal of this loss and inconvenience could be avoided were the conditions that lead to decay better understood, and if simple precautions were taken to protect the wood against it.

Decay of dead organic material is a necessary part of the sequence of natural events. During their lifetime plants are nourished by minerals and nitrogen which they absorb from the soil. When they die, and their remains decay, these nutrients are returned to the soil, thus replenishing it for the use of further plant growth.

A virgin forest, untouched by man, does not become an impenetrable mass of fallen trees, nor does the ground become covered with a thick layer of dead branches and twigs, even though vast numbers of these drop during storms and gales. Where then does all this mass of woody material go to? The answer, in short, is that it either decays or is consumed by insects. All organic materials, that is to say materials derived from plants and animals, are susceptible to decay. Some, such as flesh and fruit, decompose in a matter of hours; others, such as leaves, require months to rot away completely; while materials such as hair, cork and timber will resist decay for years, and even centuries.

All this decay is not an inherent property of the material itself. The decay is brought about by the action of micro-organisms which liquefy and digest the materials, using them as nutrients for their own growth. Even flesh can be preserved indefinitely if it is sterilised and kept in sealed containers, and such sterilisation and sealing against further infection is the basis of the canning industry.

In nature an essential function is performed by those micro-organisms that bring about the decomposition of the leaves, twigs, and branches that fall from the trees, and ultimately of the trunks themselves, when the trees die, or are brought down by storm or wind. The woody material is broken down by these tiny organisms, some of it being turned into humus which will help to nourish the young trees growing up to take the place of those that have died.

It is a mistake therefore to regard as unmitigated pests the organisms that bring about decay in our timber. Were it not for their activities no young trees could spring up in our woodlands, as the soil would be covered with a mass of fallen logs and branches. But when these organisms invade our houses or attack our stocks of timber in the yards then are they pests indeed, and all possible precautions must be taken to prevent them from doing this.

Even the less durable kinds of timber are resistant to the attack of most rotting organisms, as Wood can only be broken down by those organisms that are capable of decomposing lignified cellulose which is its principle ingredient. Most of the fungi which have this ability belong to the groups which include the toadstools and the bracket fungi. Bacteria—the minute unicellular 'germs' that cause so many of the diseases of man and animals,—are unimportant so far as the decay of wood is concerned. Of the insects that attack wood the majority thrive very much better if the timber has previously been softened by decay, and many of them are quite incapable of attacking sound dry wood.

Materials can be preserved against decay either by physical or by chemical methods. The *physical methods* are:

(*a*) keeping the material to be protected under conditions that prohibit the growth of destructive organisms, e.g. either very dry, or in cold storage; or

(*b*) keeping them in absolutely sterile conditions, as is done in the case of canned foods.

The *chemical method* is to treat the materials with antiseptics which poison any organisms that attempt to consume them.

Both physical and chemical methods are used on occasion for the preservation of timber, but the large size of most woodwork, and the uses to which it is put, usually make it impractical to protect it by physical methods from all possibility of infection. Undue worry, however, need not be felt about the spread of fungal spores (the germs of decay) if it is always borne in mind that these can germinate and set up decay only when there is a great deal of moisture present.

Decay of woodwork should never be accepted as inevitable, and if the wooden parts of a structure decay before the rest of the building that is clear evidence that the timbers were inadequately protected. Anyone designing a permanent wooden structure should give careful thought as to what protection he will give to the timber, and if there is any possibility of it becoming damp in use he should either choose a naturally durable timber or ensure that it has really adequate protection

CHAPTER I

THE NATURE AND DURABILITY OF WOOD

BEFORE deciding whether or not to apply preservatives, the properties of the timber in question must first be considered in relation to two important aspects. Firstly the durability of the wood must be ascertained, and this depends to a large extent on its inherent resistance to fungal and insect attack. Secondly it is necessary to know about its permeability to liquids. The decay resistance depends mainly on the chemical composition of the wood, while permeability is closely related to its microscopic structure.

Timber is formed in the growing tree by the accretion of rings of growth around the stem, which thus becomes thicker and thicker as it ages. Examined under the microscope wood is seen to have a cellular structure, and to be composed of cells of various shapes and sizes which perform different functions in the growing tree. The three main functions of the trunk are:

1. To transport water from the roots to the leaves; therefore part of the wood must be porous.
2. To support the branches, leaves etc.; therefore the wood must have considerable mechanical strength.
3. To act as a storehouse for the foodstuffs manufactured in the leaves.

In the relatively simple softwoods, derived from conifers, the first two functions are performed by cigar-shaped tubes known as *tracheids*. Where these are in contact with each other they are provided with small perforations, known as *pits*, which can act like valves controlling the flow of the sap. The tracheids formed during the latter part of the growing season (the summer wood) contribute more to the strength than do the thin walled tracheids of the spring wood. (See Pl. I, 2.)

In the more complicated tissues of the hardwoods, derived from broad leaved trees, there are long tubes, called *vessels*, built up like a drain pipe from numerous open ended cells. These may run direct from root to leaf providing a passage for

I

the 'express' transport of water. Mechanical strength is provided by thick walled *fibres*.

In both classes of timber reserves of food material are stored in the so-called rays, which consist of lines or 'walls' of brick-shaped cells that form ribbons of tissue running from the central pith to the bark. These ray cells are among the few cells in the wood that are truly alive, but they only remain alive for a certain number of years.

Sapwood and Heartwood

If one looks at the freshly cut end of an oak or pine log one can see a ring of pale coloured wood, an inch or so wide, below the bark, and a central core which is of a darker colour. (See Pl. I, 1.) The pale coloured outerring is called the *sapwood*, and the darker coloured core is the *heartwood*. As new rings of growth are added on to the outside rim of the sapwood the inner rings of the sapwood change into heartwood. As the living cells of the sapwood die they form chemicals, such as tannins, which usually lead to a darkening in colour of the wood, and generally increase its resistance to fungal and insect attack.

The presence and the amount of the sapwood is of great importance in relation to the need for wood preservation for two reasons: Firstly sapwood of practically all trees is readily attacked by fungal decay and wood boring insects. Secondly sapwood, which in the living tree provides the path for the flow of the sap, remains permeable to liquids even after the tree is felled and the timber has been seasoned. This means that in practice sapwood can easily be impregnated with a preservative.

The cells of the heartwood of many trees become so choked with gummy materials, and the vessels so blocked with the bladder-like outgrowths, which are called *tyloses*, that no liquid can pass through them. (See Pl. I, 3.)

It is a fortunate coincidence that the non-durable sapwood is so readily permeable by liquids for this means that the most vulnerable part of the timber is also the most easily protected. But there are some trees that do not form heartwood, and in these the older, mature wood may, as in the case of Beech, remain quite permeable, even though its colour remains much the same as that of the sapwood.

It is difficult by microscopic examination of the structure to predict, with any degree of certainty, the permeability of a wood to liquids, so practical tests have to be made to determine this property. Fortunately the results of carefully controlled tests are now available on nearly all the commercial timbers used in Europe. See Table II. It must, however, be emphasised that there may be great variation between different samples of the same kind of wood. This is particularly true, for instance, of the Douglas Fir.

Importance of Moisture Content and Seasoning

In the sapwood of a healthy tree all the cells are full of sap and the wood may contain more than its own weight of water. If the timber is to be impregnated with a preservative solution it is absolutely essential that the timber should be seasoned so as to remove all the liquid in the cells and make room for the preservative. The best way of treating green, unseasoned timber with preservative is by one of the diffusion or sap replacement processes. (See p. 44.)

Many of the failures through premature decay of creosoted timber can be attributed to the fact that the timber was not sufficiently seasoned before it was treated. Before poles and sleepers receive pressure treatment they must be piled openly for a sufficient length of time to become adequately seasoned. A moisture content of 25-30% is quite suitable for timber that is to be impregnated; while a somewhat lower moisture content may be desirable for timber that is to be treated by surface applications of preservative.

Decay Resistance

Timbers vary enormously in their resistance to decay. No wood is completely and permanently resistant to all forms of decay, but some, like Teak, Ironbark, and Sequoia, will endure for many decades or even centuries, even as posts in the ground. At the other end of the scale are the perishable woods such as Birch, the logs of which may become infected with decay before they can even be sawn up.

The basic wood substance, i.e. the lignified cellulose, that composes the walls of the fibres and other cells of the wood, does not appear to differ greatly in composition between one kind of wood and another, and one must look for some other

B

explanation of the variations in durability. Many attempts have been made to correlate durability with density, but no general correlation has been found. This is not altogether surprising when one comes to think of it. Why should a wood decay less rapidly merely because it contains more of the material from which a wood-destroying fungus can draw its nourishment? The fact that sapwood becomes much more resistant to decay as it changes into heartwood suggests that during this process some natural preservatives are formed by the tree which protect the lignocellulose of the cell walls from attack. It has indeed now been shown that the resistance to decay of the naturally durable timbers can be attributed to the presence in the heartwood of substances, such as tannins and other complex phenolic substances, that are toxic to wood destroying fungi. These substances are often referred to as 'extractives' since they can be removed from the wood by extraction with water or other solvents. The decay of a wood such as Western Red Cedar is closely related to its content of such extractives—the higher the content the more durable is the wood. But if the extractives are in any degree soluble in water then prolonged washing of the wood will render it susceptible again to attack, and this no doubt explains why thin roof shingles made of Western Red Cedar begin to decay after fifteen to twenty years' exposure. There are many hardwoods in which the substances that confer durability on the heartwood are not soluble in water and these woods retain their resistance to infection even after prolonged exposure to the weather.

Variations in Natural Durability

Wide variations in durability can occur within a single commercial species of timber. This may be due either to a varying proportion of sapwood, or to differences in the inherent decay resistance of the wood. As an example of the first type one can compare the difference between present day supplies of Baltic Redwood, which is cut from fairly small trees and therefore contains a high proportion of sapwood, with the better qualities of the same wood, cut from much larger trees, which was shipped to this country during the nineteenth century. Baltic Redwood, free from sapwood, is a moderately durable timber—the same timber containing a high percentage of pieces consisting wholly, or partly, of sapwood is a relatively perishable timber.

Differences exist in the durability even of the heartwood between one tree and another of the same species. Such differences, which are generally associated with variation in the content of extractives, are probably inherited; and it would almost certainly be possible to breed trees for their durability, just in the same way as it has been found possible to propagate rubber trees that give a far higher yield of latex than their wild ancestors in the Brazilian jungle.

In addition to the variation from tree to tree it has been found that in some trees there is a great difference in decay resistance between the inner and the outer heartwood. Such differences have been shown to exist both in conifers, such as Scots Pine and Western Red Cedar, and in hardwoods such as Oak and African Mahogany. In practically all the species where such differences have been found, the core of inner heartwood, formed when the tree was young, is less resistant to decay than the outer heartwood formed by the more mature tree. Sometimes this difference may be considerable, as in African Mahogany, where the outer heartwood yields a durable timber, while the wood from the core of the tree is very susceptible to decay. But not all trees show this sort of variation, and in some of the most durable species, such as Greenheart, the central core appears to be just as resistant to rot as is the outer heartwood.

The practical significance of these findings is that one can not define precisely the inherent natural durability of any kind of wood. One can only classify timbers broadly into classes of durability, on the basis of their known performance in use and from the results of carefully controlled tests.

Tests of Natural Durability

In the case of common, native timbers some information about their durability can be gleaned from an examination of old buildings, and other structures in the open; but in order to form an accurate estimate of the decay resistance of unfamiliar, or newly introduced, species it is necessary to make special tests on them. The earlier tests all involved placing stakes or posts in a test plot of soil—commonly known as a 'graveyard'—and examining them at regular intervals to determine how long they lasted. Many such tests have been carried out in different parts of the world, and much useful information has been gained from them. Such field tests, however, have certain disadvantages, of which the most obvious are the length of time involved, and the difficulty of making continuous observations over many years. Keeping track of large numbers of specimens among a lush growth of weeds is in itself not easy. Mowing machines and scythes obviously cannot be used and much hard work among the specimens may be necessary to prevent the 'graveyard' reverting to 'jungle'. In places where termites are present it is often difficult to decide whether these or fungal decay are responsible when the test stakes fail.

In order to avoid all these difficulties a laboratory method has been developed by which the decay resistance of a timber can be assessed in a matter of months. The method is similar to that used for determining the toxicity of wood preservatives (see p. 73). Small test pieces, carefully selected so as to sample as fairly as possible the various parts of the trunk, are exposed at a constant temperature to pure cultures of several different wood-rotting fungi. They are kept under these conditions for a given period, usually four months, and the loss in dry weight resulting from fungal decay is then measured. This figure, expressed as a percentage of the initial dry weight of the specimens gives a useful measure of the susceptibility of the wood to decay. It is important always to use several test fungi including both brown and white rots.

Classification of Timbers on Basis of Durability

It is usual to classify timber into five classes in respect to their durability, and in the following table the corresponding 'life' of a 2 ×2 inch stake, in average soil in England, is compared with the average loss in dry weight per cent suffered in laboratory tests.

Durability Class	Life of Test Stake in the Field	Average loss in Dry Weight % in Laboratory Test
Very durable	Over 25 years	Nil or negligible
Durable	15-20 ,,	Up to 5
Moderately durable	10-15 ,,	5-10
Non-durable	5-10 ,,	10-30
Perishable	Less than 5 ,,	Over 30

Cross section of pine showing sapwood and heartwood
(Crown copyright)

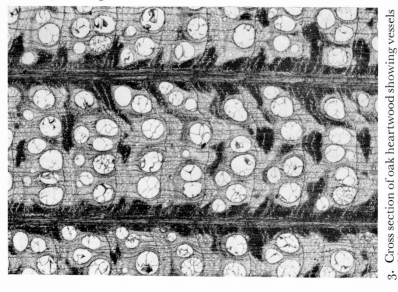

2. Cross section of pine showing annual rings of spring and summer wood. Highly magnified

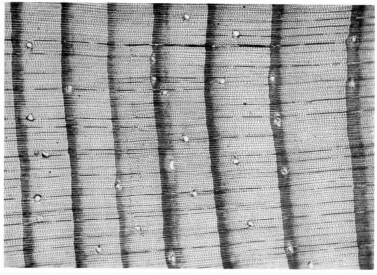

3. Cross section of oak heartwood showing vessels blocked with tyloses and wide rays. Highly magnified (*Crown copyright*)

The following are a few illustrations of the uses of timber in the various durability classes:

Very Durable

Timbers in this class may be used with confidence for permanent structures in contact with the ground or in water, e.g. transmission poles; railway sleepers; bridging timbers; marine piling; foundation timbers; hut poles and fencing.

Durable

Durable woods can be used for the exposed parts of permanent structures which are not in direct contact with the soil. They are suitable for the frames, keels, and decking of boats, for the making of vats, for window sills, and for domestic draining boards.

Moderately Durable

Woods in this class should never be used in direct contact with the soil unless given preservative treatment, but for short periods they can withstand exposure to damp conditions. They are suitable for those parts of permanent structures that are given protection against the weather, such as rafters, joists, etc., and they can also be used for vehicles and for some parts of boats, deck beams for example.

Non-Durable

Non-durable woods should always receive treatment if there is any risk of their becoming damp in use. They can safely be used for internal joinery and furniture, though, if they carry a high proportion of sapwood, they may require long term protection against insect attack.

Perishable

Timbers described as perishable require rapid extraction, conversion, and seasoning, to avoid decay in the log and while they are being dried. They should not be used for constructional work even under cover unless they have received thorough preservative treatment. They are often used in turnery, and as veneers in plywood for indoor use, and for tea chests, and for making matches and chip baskets.

It must be emphasised that there is considerable variation in durability between different samples of the same species, so that some samples of certain timbers might fall into a class above or below that in which they are normally classified. Obviously then durability cannot be estimated precisely in the case of many variable timbers which could be placed in more than one of the above classes depending on the quality of the samples examined.

The life of a timber structure depends on a great many factors, many of them unpredictable. These may involve the interaction of the timber with the weather, the soil and with various destructive agencies, and there is always an element of chance as to whether a particular insect or fungus becomes established in the wood. It is therefore unnecessary, and might in fact be misleading, to attempt to classify timbers too rigidly on the basis of their overall decay resistance.

TABLE I

CLASSIFICATION OF COMMERCIAL TIMBERS ON BASIS OF DURABILITY

Very Durable	Durable	Moderately Durable	Non-Durable	Perishable
Softwoods				
Sequoia	Western Red Cedar	Larch	Spruces	Sapwood of
Yew	Pitch Pine, best	Douglas Fir	Hemlock	Pines
		Baltic Redwood	Silver Fir	
		Yellow Pine		
Hardwoods				
Afzelia	Agba	Danta	Abura	Alder
Afrormosia	Chestnut, sweet	Mahogany, African	Ash	Beech
Greenheart	Guarea	Meranti	Elm	Birch
Iroko	Idigbo	Keruing	Obeche	Sycamore
Jarrah	Mahogany,	Sapele	Poplar	Willow
Kapur	American	Turkey Oak	Ramin	
Okan	Meranti		Seraya	
Opepe	Oak, English			
Padauk	Oak, American			
	White			
Rhodesian	Robinia			
'Teak'	Utile			
Teak				

Resistance to Insect Attack

The resistance of many tropical timbers to termite attack has been established on the basis of field tests, and also, to a more limited extent, as the result of controlled laboratory experiments. Since there are a great many kinds of termites which vary greatly in their habits, results obtained in any one territory may not be directly applicable to another part of the world.

In Europe there are very few wood-boring insects that will attack the heartwood (provided it is sound) of any of those timbers in which it is clearly defined. The Common Furniture Beetle, *Anobium punctatum*, rarely, if ever, infests the sound heartwood of Pine (Baltic Redwood), or of Oak. Death Watch Beetle, *Xestobium rufo-villosum*, becomes established only in timber in which there is incipient decay, but its larvae (grubs) may work their way from the decayed area into the adjacent sound wood. Their rate of progress in sound wood is, however, extremely slow.

Powder Post Beetles, *Lyctus spp.*, infest only the sapwood of hardwoods such as Oak, Ash, Walnut, etc. As these insects derive their nourishment entirely from the reserve food materials stored in the wood, they can flourish only in sapwood that contains a certain proportion of this starch.

To sum up—it is the proportion of sapwood in a commercial sample of timber that determines its susceptibility to attack. If the majority of pieces of wood in a consignment of timber intended for building purposes contain sapwood, then preservative treatment against insect attack is usually justified.

Significance of Natural Durability

The decision as to whether a naturally durable timber should be used, or whether preservative treatment should be given to a less durable species, will, of course, be influenced by the relative availability and cost of the different kinds of wood, and the facilities available for treating the less durable kinds, as well as the uses to which the timber in question is to be put.

In most countries there has been a shift from the use of naturally durable woods to the use of preserved timber. This is because in general the more durable kinds of wood come from relatively slow growing trees, such as Oak, Yew and Sequoia. As the natural forests of such trees are felled the tendency nowadays is to replace them with faster growing species, such as pines, spruces and poplar, which all require treatment. So we find that whereas in the Middle Ages most buildings in England were built of oak, to-day softwoods are used for nearly all constructional work.

In underdeveloped countries where there are few facilities for treating wood properly it may still be more economical to use durable local timbers for poles and railway sleepers, but in industrialised countries it is usually cheaper to use pressure treated softwood.

In Great Britain and Western Europe, where there are good facilities for treating non-durable woods, our needs for poles and sleepers are met by creosoted softwoods, but naturally durable timbers can still be used with great advantage for certain purposes. The following are some of the more important uses for which they are recommended:

1. Structural timbers of very large size which cannot be easily treated—e.g. Greenheart for marine piling.
2. Boat building in which large timbers have to be fashioned to particular shapes on the site.
3. Vats that are to contain liquids which must not be contaminated by traces of any poisonous, or strongly smelling, chemicals.
4. External decorative woodwork in which the natural colour and beauty of the untreated wood must not be lost.
5. Plywood for external and marine use.

When wood is to be used for purely temporary purposes, such as packaging, or when it is to be kept in a permanently dry situation, resistance to fungal decay is not an essential property. It is however difficult to extract and season the woods that have little or no resistance to decay, and special care has to be taken to ensure that there is no delay between felling and conversion of such perishable species as Birch and Beech and the tropical ones like Balsa, Limba and Obeche.

Permeability of Wood

Timbers vary as greatly in their permeability to liquids as they do in their natural durability. Some are so open to the passage of air and liquids that one can easily blow air through quite long sticks. Others are so dense that it is almost impossible to force any fluid into them even under a high external pressure. So before attempting to impregnate any timber with preservative it is obviously essential to know something about its permeability. The really impermeable species can, at best, be given only skin deep protection.

The sapwood of most woods is freely permeable to liquids.

A moment's reflection will show why this is so—the sapwood in the growing tree is the zone through which large volumes of sap must pass on their way from the roots of the tree to the leaves. The diameter and number of the vessels in proportion to the content of thick-walled fibres obviously affects the permeability of the wood and there are some timbers—described as vessel-porous—into which preservatives can only penetrate along the lines of the vessels.

Great changes in permeability occur when the sapwood turns into heartwood. This is due to the blockage of the vessels with tyloses and the deposit of gummy and resinous materials in the cells.

Classification of Timbers on Basis of Permeability

TABLE II

CLASSIFICATION OF TIMBERS ON BASIS OF PERMEABILITY

Permeable	Moderately Resistant to Impregnation	Resistant to Impregnation	Very Resistant to Impregnation
Alder	Ash	Balsa	Chestnut, sweet
Beech	Elm	Douglas Fir	Gaboon
Birch	Fir, silver	Elm, rock	Larch
Hornbeam	Hemlock	Obeche	Mahogany, America
Lime	Poplar, Black	Poplar spp.	Mahogany, African
Oak, American	Italian	Spruce, Norway	Oak, English
Red		Sitka	Oak, American White
Sycamore		Willow	Utile
Sapwood of			Walnut
most species			Western Red Cedar

NOTE. The above relates to the heartwood of the species listed

It is usual to classify timbers into four groups on the basis of their permeability, as follows:

Permeable

These timbers can be penetrated completely under pressure in a cylinder, and can usually be heavily impregnated by the open tank process.

Moderately Resistant to Impregnation

These timbers are fairly easy to treat. Lateral penetration of $\frac{1}{4}$ to $\frac{1}{2}$ in. can be obtained in two to three hours under pressure.

Resistant to Impregnation

These timbers require long periods to obtain lateral penetration of $\frac{1}{8}$ to $\frac{3}{4}$ in. To get any worthwhile absorption they need to be incised.

Extremely Resistant, or Impermeable

No worthwhile absorption of preservative can be obtained in these timbers, even after prolonged exposure to pressure, and their impregnation by cylinder treatment should not be attempted.

There may be considerable variations in permeability between different samples of the same species—for instance Douglas Fir grown in the Rocky Mountains is much more resistant to impregnation than that grown near the coast. Again, differences in permeability may be found in samples cut from the same tree if the wood has been seasoned in a different way, or has been allowed to become infected with moulds during seasoning. These differences may have more pronounced effect on the uptake of preservatives when they are applied by brushing or dipping than when pressure is used to force the liquid into the wood.

Recent investigations at Princes Risborough have shown that water storage markedly increases the permeability of softwoods to impregnation. The following absorptions were obtained on matched material which was seasoned with and without a preliminary storage under water:

Timber	Amount of Preservative Absorbed lbs./cubic ft.		
	Air dried only	Stored under water before air drying	
		3 months	6 months
Sitka Spruce	9	23	31
Douglas Fir	2		13
Japanese Larch	4		17

The penetration was deeper and more uniform in the water stored material than in the unsoaked samples, the improvement in penetration being particularly noticeable in the spring wood.

In all kinds of wood the penetration along the grain (i.e. parallel to the direction of the vessels and fibres) is very much greater than laterally across the grain. The ratio of the longitudinal to the side penetration varies somewhat according to the kind of wood and the type of liquid. An average ratio of 15 to 1 for oily preservatives and 20 to 1 for water-borne preservatives may be taken as typical.

The rate of movement of liquids across the grain depends to some extent on the way in which the piece of wood has been cut relative to the circumferance (bark) of the tree. In pines where the rays contain resin ducts radial penetration may be several times greater than tangential, whereas in some other softwoods the tangential penetration may be greater.

Rough sawn timber absorbs liquids somewhat more rapidly than does planed timber, doubtless because the sawn timber presents more open ended cells than does the smooth surface.

CHAPTER II

AGENCIES OF DESTRUCTION

TIMBER does not deteriorate as a result of ageing alone. It does not just 'perish', in the way, for instance, that rubber 'perishes'. Its destruction or deterioration is always the result of some outside cause and if timber is adequately protected against dampness, infection and fire it will (unless exposed to exceptionally heavy wear) last almost indefinitely.

The major destructive influences to which timber is exposed in use may be listed as follows:

Fire

Timbers vary considerably in the ease with which they can be ignited and in the rate at which they will burn. Means for reducing the flammability of wood will be discussed in Chapter XIII.

Wear

In certain situations, as in a floor exposed to heavy traffic, the resistance of the timber to mechanical abrasion will determine its durability in use. The provision of a surface coating of wax or polish can greatly reduce the rate of wear of flooring or furniture.

Chemical Attack

Wood can be decomposed by prolonged exposure to strong acids or alkalis. Timbers vary in their resistance to chemical attack, and resistant species should be chosen for vats and flooring in chemical factories.

Insect Attack

In temperate countries wood-boring insects can cause serious damage to certain timbers in buildings, though the damage that they cause to exposed woodwork and to timber in contact with the soil is only a fraction of that caused by fungi. In warmer countries where termites abound, insects are often the major cause of timber destruction.

1. Piece of softwood attacked by *Merulius lacrymans*—dry rot
(Crown copyright)

2. Fruit body of *Merulius lacrymans*

Marine Borers

As the name implies these animals infest timber in the sea, or in brackish water, but do not attack timber in fresh water. Under tropical conditions the shipworm can rapidly cause extensive damage, and even in the seas of Northern Europe marine borers cause significant damage to marine structures.

Fungal Decay

The durability of timber exposed to the weather or in contact with the soil is so largely influenced by its resistance to fungal decay that the term 'durability' is often thought to be synonymous with decay resistance, though actually it has a wider meaning than this. In order to understand the need for timber preservation one must know something about the nature of the fungi that rot wood and of the conditions under which they flourish.

WOOD-ROTTING FUNGI

It is important to realise that fungal decay may be proceeding quite rapidly in timber on which no signs of fungus growth are visible. The spores of fungi, which fulfil the function of seeds, are extremely minute, and are individually invisible to the naked eye. On germination these spores give rise to extremely fine threads, known as hyphae, which permeate the wood and can easily be seen under the microscope. Under very damp conditions, as in an unventilated cellar, these hyphae may proliferate on the surface of the decaying wood, and give rise to a visible mass of growth which is known as mycelium (the 'spawn' of the mushroom grower). After a fungus has been growing in the wood for a period varying from weeks to years it usually forms, on the surface of the wood, a fruiting body (known technically as a 'sporophore'), which bears the reproduction cells or spores. (See Pl. II, 2 and 3.)

Fungi are classified according to the nature of their fruiting bodies. Most wood-rotting fungi belong to the group called Basidiomycetes which produce fruit bodies of appreciable size in the form of toadstools, brackets, or skins; but the type of decay known as Soft Rot may be caused by mould-like microfungi, which form their spores as a mere powdery growth on the surface of the wood.

Fungi are capable of extremely rapid multiplication, their fruiting bodies producing in a short time myriads of minute spores which drift about in the air spreading infection far and wide. It has been estimated that a fruiting body of one of the larger bracket fungi may produce over eight hundred million spores per hour over a period of months, and that a fruiting body of the Dry Rot Fungus one yard across may produce fifty million spores a minute over a period of several days.

The practical significance of all this vast production of spores is that any piece of wood in the open, and even the timber in buildings, must sooner or later become infected with the spores of some fungus. This is not quite so alarming as it sounds when it is remembered that only those spores that fall on wood containing more than a certain percentage of moisture can actually germinate.

Conditions Necessary for Fungal Growth and Decay

Fungi are a form of plant life and, with one important exception, require similar conditions for their growth, i.e. a suitable medium on which to grow, moisture, warmth and air. Unlike green plants they do not require light, for they lack the green colouring matter (chlorophyll) by means of which green plants are able to build up organic matter from the carbon dioxide in the atmosphere. Fungi, however, must have organic matter on which to live so they grow directly on living plants or animals or on their dead remains. They cannot live on purely mineral soil. The fungi that grow on living plants are called *parasites*; those that grow on dead material are known as *saprophytes*. Most plant diseases (including almost all the important diseases of trees) are caused by fungi. Some of the decay that may be found in sawn timber originates as a heart rot in the standing tree. Before timber is treated with any preservative it should be examined for signs of previous decay in the tree stage. (See Pl. II, 5.)

The factor that in practice usually determines whether timber in use remains sound or becomes decayed is the moisture content of the wood. Freshly felled green timber may contain its own weight of water and, unless this moisture is allowed to evaporate by seasoning, decay can quickly become established. (See Chapter XII.) If seasoned timber is allowed to pick up moisture, either by exposure to the rain or, as in a building, from leakage of water, or if it is used in contact with the soil, it again becomes susceptible to attack.

Different species of wood-rotting fungi vary somewhat in their moisture requirements which depend to some extent on the density of the wood involved. In general timber is susceptible to attack at any moisture content between what is known as 'fibre saturation point', which is when the walls of the cells are saturated, and complete saturation of the wood, which is when the cell cavities are filled with water—a condition commonly known as 'waterlogged'. Translating this into figures means that wood is susceptible to attack when its moisture content (based on the oven dry weight) lies between about 27% and 100% or above. The optimum moisture content for the growth of most wood-rotting fungi in softwoods lies between about 35% and 75%, and the absolute minimum is about 22%. No figure can be given for the maximum as this depends so much on the density of the wood itself.

Some fungi are extremely resistant to desiccation and can survive for very long periods in completely air dry wood. In controlled laboratory experiments it was found that a species that normally grows on exposed fencing survived ten years on samples of wood kept in a dry room and having a moisture content of only 12%. In practice this means that even when decay has been stopped by drying out the woodwork it is not for very many years that the fungus can be assumed to be dead, and should the timber at any time be rewetted the rot will start again and spread out from the point where it was arrested.

Fortunately the Dry Rot Fungus is rather more susceptible to desiccation and in completely dry wood will die out in about six to nine months.

Fungi are aerobic organisms—that is to say they require oxygen for their respiration and so they cannot make any appreciable amount of growth in wood that is fully saturated with water. Wood, therefore, can be kept in a sound condition for an indefinite period if it is submerged under water or immersed in an impermeable clay. In such conditions, however, it will in the course of centuries become very dark in colour and undergo certain slow chemical changes. The so-called 'bog oak', for instance, that is dug out of swamps is almost coal black.

Temperature has an important effect on the growth of fungi and, within the normal range of a temperate climate, the warmer it is the faster they grow. In cold weather growth is very slow, and little or no growth can occur at freezing point. For this reason it is easy during the winter to extract logs free of decay from the forests in Canada and Scandinavia. In West Africa, on the other hand, special precautions have to be taken in order to obtain clean logs of the more perishable species which can easily become infected before they reach the sawmill. (See Chapter XII.)

While cold checks the growth of all fungi, freezing does not actually kill fungi in wood, and they soon become active again when the wood thaws out. On the other hand most of them are soon killed by exposure to high temperatures, and a convenient way of sterilising infected timber is to heat it in a timber drying kiln to a temperature of 150°F. The killing effect of heat is much more pronounced in a humid atmosphere, so that the humidity should be kept as high as possible when attempting to sterilise timber in this way. High humidity will also minimise the risk of surface drying of the wood with consequent splitting.

Effects of Fungal Decay on Wood

Chemical Effects. Fungi decompose wood by secreting acids and enzymes (ferments) which, in the presence of moisture, render soluble some of the cellulose and other constituents of the wood. These are then absorbed and used as nutrients by the fungus. Much of the wood substance may thus be changed in composition and texture before it is actually absorbed by the fungus. This is why the strength of wood may be seriously affected at quite an early stage of decay. Like other organisms that require air, fungi respire and give off carbon dioxide. During this process water is also formed, so that, once an attack is established, the wood tends to get moister, thus accelerating the growth of the fungus. The chemical reaction involved can be expressed by considering the oxidation of glucose sugar derived from the cellulose in the wood, as follows:

Glucose plus oxygen = carbon dioxide and water

$$C_6H_{12}O_6 + 6O_2 = 6(CO_2) + 6H_2O$$

3. Fruit body of a wood-rotting Agaric *(Crown copyright)*

4. Cooling-tower slat showing effect of soft rot. Transverse section at right shows superficial nature of this rot *(Crown copyright)*

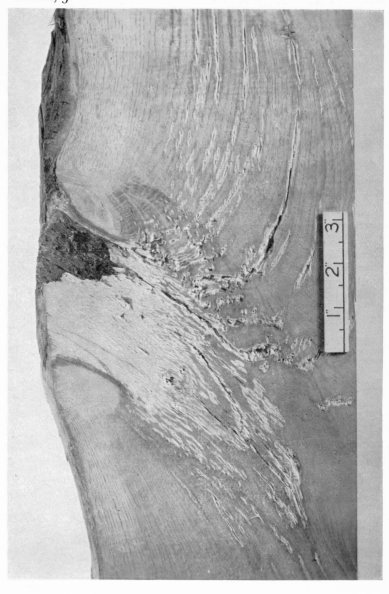

Fungi also produce organic acids which can accelerate the corrosion of any metal in contact with the decaying wood; and certain fungi produce aromatic substances which give a characteristic smell to the wood which they decay. *Lentinus lepidus*, for instance, which is the fungus usually responsible for decay in inadequately creosoted sleepers and poles, produces a pleasant sweet smell reminiscent of balsam.

Physical Effects. Everyone knows that rotten wood is soft and crumbles easily at a touch. (See Pl. II, 1.) What is perhaps not so well known is that even slight incipient decay greatly reduces the strength of the wood. It rapidly loses its toughness, becoming brittle and therefore less resistant to sudden stresses. It is, therefore, particularly important that only absolutely sound timber should be used for such things as ladders, vehicles and sports goods.

As decay proceeds wood substance is used up by the fungi and the wood becomes lighter in weight and begins to shrink. This shrinkage and loss in dry weight may not be very noticeable so long as the wood is in a wet condition but become obvious as soon as the decayed wood is dried out. (See Pl. II, 4.)

Fungal decay greatly increases the permeability of the wood to liquids. This means that any exposed woodwork quickly absorbs and retains moisture whenever there is any rain, and the wetter the wood the faster will the decay proceed. However this increased porosity of decayed wood has one favourable result in that any areas of incipient decay in wood that is being treated with a preservative readily absorb the fluid, and the infected zone thus becomes sterilised and any further spread of the rot is usually prevented.

The colour of wood also is usually affected by fungal decay. It becomes darker in the case of the brown rots which decompose only the cellulose, and is made lighter by the white rots which attack all the constituents of the wood. Bluish grey streaks and patches are not an indication of decay, but are generally due to the growth in the wood of fungi of the mould type. (See p. 140.) Narrow dark lines running through the wood are, however, a certain indication of incipient decay. These so-called 'zone lines' are most often seen in hardwoods such as beech, maple and ash.

Decayed wood is much more easily ignited than sound wood,

c

and fires in buildings are occasionally started when painters using blowlamps to remove old paint come to a patch of decayed wood in a sill or soffit board. Preservation of wood may thus in itself tend to reduce its flammability, and by mixing fire retardant chemicals with wood preservatives the risk of any wood structure catching fire can be greatly reduced. (See Chapter XIII.)

Decay renders wood much more susceptible to attack by wood-boring insects and indeed there are many species that cannot infest sound wood. The larvae of some beetles survive for quite long periods in sound wood but only make extremely slow growth. By preventing decay in structural timber the risk of infestation by Death Watch Beetle is greatly reduced if not entirely eliminated.

WOOD-DESTROYING INSECTS

The occurrence and severity of insect damage to timber is much more erratic and less predictable than is that of fungal decay. One can forecast with some degree of certainty that, given a sufficiently long exposure to damp conditions, any perishable wood will decay. The spores of fungi are produced in such vast numbers, and are distributed so widely by air currents, that sooner or later some of them will find their way on to almost any and every piece of timber, not only in the open but also inside buildings. If conditions are suitable for their growth, i.e. if the wood is sufficiently damp and of a susceptible variety, they will germinate and set up decay.

In the case of insects, however, timber can become infested only if the females can find their way to it and deposit fertile eggs in such positions that the newly-hatched larvae can penetrate into the wood and thrive therein. (See Pl. II, 6.) The natural habitat of timber insects is in the dead and dying parts of standing trees and in fallen logs. Some of the wood-boring beetles are not strong flyers and so they seldom reach buildings in the centre of towns and cities by flying there directly from surrounding woodlands. Probably they are most frequently introduced into town buildings in old already infected timber and furniture.

Insects have sensitive powers of discrimination and, as they can move about freely, they can select, for laying their eggs, the kinds of wood most favourable for the growth of their larvae.

The nutritional requirements of wood-boring insects vary greatly, and it is difficult to generalise about their needs. Some insects are (like the cow) able to digest cellulose with the help of micro-organisms in their gut; others feed on the starch in sapwood; others again live mainly on microscopic fungi that flourish in their tunnels.

In all those timbers in which it is clearly differentiated heart-wood is always much more resistant to insect attack than is sapwood. There are two reasons for this: firstly heartwood contains little or no reserve food material, such as starch, which can easily be digested by the insects; and secondly it is often impregnated with tannins, and other phenolic substances, which are as toxic to insects as they are to fungi.

One could classify the insects that infest timber in a number of different ways, e.g.

1. By the natural orders of insects to which they belong—beetles, termites, ants, moths, etc.
2. According to the stage at which they attack the wood—as trees, logs, seasoning piles, timber in use, etc.
3. According to their mode of nutrition—cellulose feeders, starch feeders, fungus feeders etc.

Nearly all the insects that cause serious damage to timber belong to one or other of the two orders:

Coleoptera—the beetles
Isoptera   —the termites or 'white ants'.

There are in addition a few caterpillars of moths, *Lepidoptera*, which occur in trees, and several species of *Hymenoptera*—the wood wasps—which occasionally cause some damage.

From the wood preservation aspect it is most convenient to consider insects according to the stage at which they attack the wood, but protection against termites presents many special problems as they are able to attack timber in all its stages. Termites occur to a limited extent in Southern Europe but are not found in Great Britain. In many tropical countries they cause untold damage to all kinds of timber structures. European manufacturers of wooden articles that are to be exported to such countries are, of course, often concerned with how best to render their goods proof against termite attack.

Insects that Attack Logs

Of the insects that attack freshly-felled logs the Pinhole Borers (or Ambrosia Beetles) are a more serious menace in the tropics than they are in temperate countries. Hardwoods affected by these insects are, however, often imported into the United Kingdom and though the beetles do not breed in this country and the damage does not spread, the evident signs of insect attack alarm purchasers and users of timber and thereby reduce the commercial value of any infected timber.

Pinhole Borers, of which there are many species, belong to the natural orders Platypodidae and Scolytidae, and they vary in size from a twenty-fifth to a ninth of an inch in length. They are all pests of unseasoned timber, generally attacking freshly-felled logs. They do not derive any nourishment from the wood itself but feed on certain moulds (the 'ambrosia' from which they derive their second name) which grow on the walls of the tunnels which they make in the wood. Since these moulds can grow only in unseasoned timber it follows that the beetles themselves cannot breed or survive for long in seasoned timber. The holes they have made remain as an indication of past infestation, but seasoned timber showing this defect can safely be used as there will be no risk of the damage increasing or spreading to other timber. The characteristic features of Pinhole Borer damage are given in Table III and measures for the protection of logs are described in Chapter XII.

Insects that Attack Timber during Seasoning and Storage

The most troublesome pests of sawn timber during its seasoning and storage prior to manufacture are the Powder Post Beetles, which belong to the *Lyctidae* family. At least six species of *Lyctus* have been found in this country of which *Lyctus brunneus* is by far the commonest. These beetles are black or reddish brown, about a fifth of an inch in length, and are elongated with a somewhat streamlined appearance. The curved white larvae grow to about a quarter of an inch long and they have a characteristic small brown patch near the rear end of the body, which is visible with the aid of a lens.

Four stages in life of Longhorn Beetle—egg, larva, pupa, adult

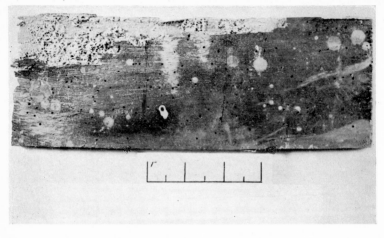

(above and left)

Damage caused by Common Furniture Beetle

The female beetles lay their long thin eggs within the pores of hardwoods, such as Oak, Ash, and Elm, that have fairly large vessels. The larvae tunnel freely in the sapwood and may eventually reduce it to powder. However they usually leave a thin surface skin of wood intact which means that infestation may not be detected until mature beetles make their exit holes. Heartwood is not normally attacked though mature beetles may tunnel out through it. The bore dust made by these insects is exceedingly fine, almost like flour, and one often sees little conical piles of this dust on the surface of boards in which larvae are actively working. The characteristic features of Powder Post Beetle attack are given in Table III.

These larvae cannot digest cellulose and they derive their nourishment from the starch stored in the sapwood. Hardwoods that contain a lot of starch such as Obeche and Limba are therefore particularly susceptible to attack. Suitable preservative treatments to prevent attack are described in Chapter XII.

Insects that Attack Timber in Buildings

In this country there are two major pests that infest timber in buildings—the Common Furniture Beetle and the Death Watch Beetle, both belonging to the *Anobiidae* family. A serious pest of buildings in Europe, the House Longhorn, is prevalent here only within a limited area in west Surrey.

The Common Furniture Beetle—Anobium punctatum—is, in this country, by far the most common cause of the damage attributed to 'woodworm'. The small dark brown beetles which emerge during the summer months measure from a tenth to a fifth of an inch in length and can fly quite actively, particularly on warm sunny days. After mating the female beetle lays her eggs on exposed rough surfaces of wood, plywood, or wicker work. After four to five weeks the eggs hatch and the young larvae penetrate into the wood. There they may spend three years or longer, tunnelling and growing in size, until they pupate and finally emerge as adult beetles through exit holes one-sixteenth of an inch in diameter. (See Pl. II, 7.) Each of the holes that can be seen on infested wood indicates the place where a beetle has emerged. The adult beetles do not again bore into the wood.

As infestations are likely to remain undetected until a sufficiently large number of exit holes have appeared to attract attention, it used to be thought that newly-seasoned timber was immune to attack, and that timber had to mature before it became susceptible to woodworm. However, recent investigations at Forest Products Research Laboratory, and the discovery of woodworm in newly built houses indicate that this is not the case. On the contrary there is some evidence that timber becomes less susceptible to attack as it ages until in really old wood the attacks may eventually cease altogether. The characteristic features of wood attacked by Furniture Beetle are given in Table III.

The natural habitat of Anobiid beetles is the dead portions of old trees where the moisture content of the wood will seldom, if ever, fall below 18-20% and may often be much higher. In a well-built house the moisture content of the woodwork will normally be considerbly lower than this. Consequently the larvae develop more slowly except where locally damp conditions exist, as in cellars, under stairs, in skirting boards and panelling on damp walls. Decayed wood is more susceptible to attack than is sound timber. It is generally believed that there is more woodworm damage in buildings in the more humid western regions of the British Isles than in the dryer eastern half of the country. Some seaside towns on the south coast are well known to have a high proportion of their buildings infested with woodworm.

The Death Watch Beetle—*Xestobium rufovillosum*—is the largest of the British Anobiids, measuring a quarter to a third of an inch in length. It is a dark brown, rather sturdily built beetle, somewhat sluggish in its movements, and has never been observed actively flying. It is primarily a pest of large-sized timbers in old buildings, such as churches, in which damp has been allowed to reach the woodwork. It is rare in the north of England and unknown in Scotland. The tapping sound which the adults make in spring and early summer is probably a mating call. The eggs are laid in cracks and crevices on exposed wooden surfaces, and the larvae tunnel into the wood where they remain for a number of years depending on how favourable conditions are for their development. Their final size is similar to or slightly larger than, that of the adult beetles.

After pupation the beetles emerge through exit holes an eighth of an inch across.

The natural habitat of the Death Watch Beetle is in the decayed parts of trunks, and large branches, of oak and certain other hardwoods. It rarely, if ever, attacks sound timber, and when larvae are found in sound portions of a beam it will generally be observed that they have worked their way from another part in which there was already fungal decay. Prevention of attack by these beetles depends then primarily on adequate protection of the timber against fungal decay, and this means guarding against the woodwork becoming damp, and using wood preservatives in situations where the access of moisture is unavoidable. As the attack is usually in large-sized timbers it is difficult to eradicate the insects by the use of insecticidal solutions. Injection of fluids under pressure through holes bored in the wood is often used to increase the penetration. Probably fumigation with a gas that is toxic to insects is the most effective way of treating large structural timbers. Repeated fumigation of H.M.S. *Victory* with methyl bromide greatly reduced the infestation in the hull of the ship.

The Longhorn Beetles, which belong to the *Cerambycidae* family, are mostly forest insects which breed in the trunks of sickly or freshly felled trees. Occasionally larvae of these insects occur in sawn timber from which they emerge as beetles several years after the wood has been used for building. As a rule they never re-infest seasoned timber, but there is one species, *Hylotrupes bajulus*, which attacks seasoned wood and breeds in houses. It is a major pest in parts of Europe, particularly in north-west Germany and Denmark where it has caused severe structural damage in the roof timbers of many houses. Recently there have been reports that the insect is causing increasing damage in France and the Low Countries, but so far in England it appears only to have caused serious damage in parts of west Surrey.

This beetle, which is brown or blackish, and measures half an inch or more in length, is provided with two long antennae. The straight white larvae may be over one inch long when fully grown. The beetles emerge in late summer making oval exit holes a quarter of an inch or more in diameter.

House Longhorn damage is confined to the sapwood, but

this may completely disintegrate, so that joists which contain a high proportion of sapwood may actually collapse as a result of the attack.

In those towns where House Longhorn damage has been widespread by-laws have been passed which stipulate that the pest must be eradicated, and that all new timber used in new buildings or for repairs to existing ones, shall receive effective preservative treatment.

TABLE III

CHARACTERISTICS FOR DISTINGUISHING SOME OF THE COMMONER WOOD-BORING BEETLES

(reproduced from Forest Products Research Leaflet No. 8)

Insect	Timbers Attacked	Exit Holes	Bore Dust
Common Furniture Beetle	Seasoned hardwoods and softwoods, sound or decayed. Usually sapwood only	Circular Approx. $\frac{1}{16}$ in. diameter	Ellipsoidal pellets
Death Watch Beetle	Old decayed hardwoods; softwoods rarely. Heartwood and sapwood	Circular Approx. $\frac{1}{8}$ in. diameter	Coarse bun-shaped pellets
Lyctus Powder Post Beetle	Seasoned and partly seasoned sound hardwoods. Usually sapwood only, but emergence may occur through heartwood	Circular Approx. $\frac{1}{16}$ in. diameter	Fine talcum-like powder
House Longhorn Beetle	Seasoned sound softwoods, usually sapwood only	Oval Approx. $\frac{1}{4} \times \frac{1}{8}$ in. diameter	Larger compact cylindrical pellets and powder
Ambrosia (Pinhole-Borer) Beetle	Unseasoned sound hardwoods and softwoods	Circular entrance holes. Variable in diameter according to species of insect, but approx. $\frac{1}{50}-\frac{1}{8}$ in. diameter	Absent, but tunnels darkly stained, the stain sometimes spreading into surrounding wood
Wood-boring Weevils	Seasoned hardwoods and softwoods, decayed or very damp	Irregularly oval of varying size, approx. $\frac{1}{32}-\frac{1}{16}$ inch	Ellipsoidal pellets, smaller than those produced by full-grown Anobium larvae

The Termites—Isoptera—do not occur naturally in this country but there is some risk that they may be introduced and become established in centrally heated buildings, as they have already done in Hamburg. Logs containing living Termites are occasionally landed in the docks.

Termites are social insects, living in large colonies, and in many ways behaving in a similar fashion to the true ants. There are two main groups—the Earth-Dwelling which build their nests in the ground, or in mounds above the ground; and the Wood-Dwelling group which live in wood and do not require any contact with the soil.

A certain amount of protection can be provided against Subterranean Termites by fixing metal termite guards on the posts that support the buildings; but effective and permanent protection against Dry-wood Termites involves thorough treatment of the timber with a wood preservative which is known to be effective against them. Creosote is probably the best one in places where its colour, smell and oiliness are no objection. The most effective waterborne preservatives against Termites are those that contain a fair proportion of arsenic, while timber that has been treated with adequate amounts of borax and boric acid shows a high resistance to many species. Control methods have to be adapted to the particular breed of Termites involved as they do not all respond in the same way to different preservatives. So wide is the range of problems involved in dealing with this particular pest that it is impossible to consider them all here. For further information reference should be made to the bulletin by W. D. Macgregor (1950) and to the books by T. E. Snyders (1948) and R. V. Harris (1961).

Manufacturers in Great Britain who are exporting furniture and other articles made of wood (and other cellulose materials) to the tropics should find out whether Dry-wood Termites occur in the countries for which they are destined. If they are found to be prevalent it may be more convenient to make the articles from a timber that is naturally resistant to attack rather than to apply a wood preservative. The following timbers are known to be resistant to Termite attack: Afzelia, Cedrela (Cigar-box Cedar), Afrormosia, Iroko, Merbau, Muninga, Opepe, and Teak.

MARINE BORERS

The destruction of wood in the sea is mainly due to the activity of Marine Borers of which there are two types—bivalve molluscs (Shipworms), and small crustaceans (Gribble). Although there are a number of marine fungi which can cause slow superficial decay of cordage and timber these are of minor importance, except in so far as they pave the way for the Borer attack.

The Shipworms, known as *Teredo*, are the most destructive of the Marine Borers, and there are three species of these which are found in British waters. They start life as tiny free-swimming larvae which appear to be attracted to wood on which they soon settle down and begin to bore. The larvae soon change into the adult form, the shell altering to become an efficient cutting tool, instead of a protective coating, and the body becoming long and wormlike—hence the name 'shipworm'. Two tubes, through which the animal can circulate water around its body, project a short way out in the water from a small hole in the wood. The animal can withdraw these tubes and thus close the opening, thereby retaining water in the burrow and enabling it to survive quite long exposures to air. As the creature grows so the diameter of the burrow enlarges, sometimes reaching as much as a quarter of an inch. The tunnels twist and turn, never actually crossing, until finally the wood may become riddled with holes, although the surface remains practically intact.

Shipworms occur all around the coasts of Great Britain south of the Clyde and Forth, but only do serious harm around the southern half of England. The damage they cause is somewhat sporadic and its intensity seems to depend mainly on the temperature of the water. In warm seas they can cause surprisingly rapid damage. They cannot live in fresh water but they can survive in brackish water if it contains over about 7 parts of salt per 1000 of water. (The average salinity of sea water is 35 parts per 1000.) There is little risk of Teredo attack in water that is heavily polluted with silt, sewage or factory effluents.

Gribble, the crustacean type of wood borers, are very common all around the coasts of Great Britain. The true Gribble, *Limnoria lignorum*, which is about a sixth of an inch long and looks something like a small woodlouse, makes its burrows on the surface of the wood so that the damage it causes is always obvious. Its attack is most severe about low water level. Recent investigations suggest that incipient fungal decay of the surface layers of the wood greatly increases its susceptibility to Gribble attack. In fact some workers in this field maintain that Gribble can only become established in timber after there has been some prior infection of the wood by marine fungi.

Though no timber is completely immune to the attack of Marine Borers there are a number of species that are highly resistant, especially in temperate seas, and these can be used for marine structures without preservative treatment. They include Greenheart, Pyinkado, Turpentine, Totara and Angelique.

Full cell impregnation with coal tar creosote gives consistently effective protection against Teredo. Round piling that contains a belt of permeable sapwood is much more easily protected than are square piles that have heartwood on the exposed faces.

Metal sheathing has long been used to protect ships against Shipworm attack. Piling can be more conveniently protected by a casing of concrete applied to strong wire netting or expanded metal wrapped around the piles.

Weathering

Sometimes the surface of exposed wood begins to disintegrate and erode even when there has been no insect damage nor any evidence of fungal decay. The primary cause of such deterioration, which is known as 'weathering', is the repeated swelling and shrinking of the surface layers of the wood. Exposed surfaces absorb moisture very quickly in a damp atmosphere or during wet weather, and then they swell up before the corresponding change takes place in the interior of the wood. Thus tensions and stresses develop between the surface layers and the deep layers which lead to splits and checks and eventually to the disintegration of the whole surface. Freezing of water in the pores of the wood will also assist in this breaking up of the surface layers, and so will the abrasive action of windblown sand and chemical changes induced by ultraviolet radiation. In persistently damp situations superficial decay of the soft rot type may also accelerate the breakdown of the surface. Superficial decay of thin material such as roofing shingles has often been attributed to weathering but this, in fact, is more often the result of fungal attack.

Woods vary considerably in their susceptibility to weathering influences. Close grained dense woods containing a fair proportion of resin, or gummy materials that check the absorption and loss of water, resist weathering much better than porous open grained wood. Timbers such as Teak which move but little on wetting or drying suffer less severely than species that respond more vigorously.

Means for the prevention of weathering are described on page 101.

REFERENCES

Cartwright, K. St. G., and Findlay, W. P. K. *Decay of Timber and its Prevention*, 2nd edition, H.M.S.O., London, 1958.

Findlay, W. P. K. *Dry Rot and other Timber Troubles*, London, 1953.

Findlay, W. P. K. and Savory, J. G. 'Dry Rot in Wood', *For. Prod. Res. Bull.*, 6th edition, 1960, H.M.S.O.

Forest Products Research Laboratory Leaflets Nos. 3, 4, 6, 8, 14.

Harris W. V. *Termites. Their Recognition and Control*. London 1961.

Macgregor, W. D. 'The Protection of Buildings and Timber against Termites', *For. Prod. Res. Bull.*, 24, H.M.S.O., 1950.

Snyder, T. E. *Our Enemy the Termite*, 2nd edition, New York, 1948.

1. Transmission poles in Thailand entering cylinder prior to impregnation with Celcure

2. Building timber in Australia piled on bogey entering an 8ft. diameter cylinder

PRESERVATIVE METHODS

Wood can be protected against deterioration either by putting on a physical barrier, such as a layer of paint or varnish, which prevents any destructive agency from reaching its surface, or by making conditions in the wood unsuitable for the development and growth of wood-destroying organisms. In the latter case such conditions may be achieved by purely physical means, such as keeping the wood cold or dry, or else by chemical treatments which render it poisonous or indigestible to any pests.

The term 'wood preservation' is generally used to imply the use of some chemical, or mixture of chemicals, which is poisonous to the wood-destroying organisms; but before describing these chemical methods the purely physical means of preventing attack must first be considered.

Drying

The drying of foodstuffs, such as fruit, fish, meat and vegetables, as a means of preserving them, has been practised since the earliest times, and timber also can be preserved almost indefinitely in a similar way, provided that it is always kept dry after it has been properly seasoned. Unfortunately if dried material is rewetted it again becomes susceptible to attack however long it may have been seasoned, or however dry it may once have been. Timber is, in a certain degree, hygroscopic, and quickly takes up moisture from a damp atmosphere until it reaches a certain equilibrium moisture content. If the period during which the timber remains wet is very short the wood-rotting fungi will not have a chance to become established, but if the damp conditions persist for any length of time amounting to several weeks or months, then decay will inevitably follow.

In practice this means that one can rely on dryness to preserve susceptible timber against decay only when the latter is fully protected against the weather and is not in contact with the soil or with damp masonry, i.e. used for internal joinery or furniture.

Timbers of large dimensions dry out very slowly and there may be a risk of deterioration during the process of seasoning— see Chapter XII. This is particularly likely to occur if the trees contain incipient decay when they are felled. Toadstools have been seen growing out of large oak beams some four years after they were built into a house. Similarly the larvae of some wood-borers can survive from five to ten years in air dry wood.

The decision whether or not to rely on dryness alone to preserve the timber must depend on the architect's or designer's assessment of the risk of moisture reaching the woodwork during the life of the structure, either from condensation, or leakage, or from any cause whatsoever.

When timber containing much sapwood, which is susceptible to insect attack, is to be used, the risk from wood borers must also be taken into account, as some of these insects are able to develop in timber that would be considered dry by any ordinary standards.

Absence of Air

Since wood-rotting fungi are aerobic organisms requiring oxygen for their growth, timber kept permanently submerged in water will remain sound for long periods, except for slight surface softening which is unimportant in the case of large-sized pieces. Therefore the best way to preserve logs or large baulks of timber awaiting conversion at a sawmill is to keep them submerged in a log pond. See Chapter XII.

Preservation with Chemicals

Before deciding which wood preservative to use some thought must be given as to what degree of preservation will be necessary to ensure the length of service life required, and also to the means available for applying the preservative. Preservatives commercially available at the present time are discussed in Chapter IV; the means by which these can be applied are considered below.

The effectiveness of any preservative treatment depends not only on the nature of the preservative itself, but also on the amount taken up per unit volume of wood and the depth of its penetration. However potent a preservative may be, it cannot effectively continue to protect a piece of timber unless it is present in adequate amounts and to such a depth that the zone of treated wood on the outside effectively protects any untreated wood in the core even should there be some mechanical damage or wear on the surface. If prolonged protection is required it is essential that the preservative should penetrate into the wood to such a depth that any subsequent splitting which may occur during very dry weather does not expose untreated wood.

The amount of preservative required to protect a given unit volume of wood against any particular fungus can be determined in the laboratory and is called the *toxic limit* or *threshold value*. While this figure may be used to compare the inherent toxicities of different preservatives, and may act as a guide to the concentration required in practice, the values obtained in laboratory tests cannot be used directly to specify the retention required for commercial timbers. This is particularly the case when the preservative is slightly volatile so that its concentration in the wood tends to fall with the passage of time.

Broadly speaking preservative treatments are of four types:

1. Non-pressure treatment, in which the wood is treated by brushing, spraying or steeping.
2. Pressure treatments, in which the pieces of timber are impregnated under considerable pressure in a closed cylinder or by atmospheric pressure in the so-called 'hot and cold open tank process'.
3. Diffusion treatments, in which unseasoned or wet timber is allowed to remain in contact with strong solutions of salts which diffuse throughout its thickness.
4. Sap replacement methods. These are only applied to freshly felled logs.

NON-PRESSURE TREATMENTS

Brush Treatments

Brushing is a convenient way of applying a wood preservative to small individual items, such as sheds, wheelbarrows, etc. It is the obvious choice for the amateur who does not possess spraying equipment or dipping tanks. Joinery and furniture infected with woodworm are also usually treated by brushing the insecticide freely over the surface.

When it is desirable to apply a preservative to timber already in situ in a building, brush application is often the only means available, especially if the timbers to be treated lie above a ceiling which must not be stained with the fluid, as would happen if a spray were used.

When applying preservative with a brush the surface of the wood should be flooded with the liquid so as to get the maximum amount absorbed. It should never be brushed on thinly like a paint. Oily preservatives should be applied only to thoroughly dry timber, and care should be taken to fill with fluid all cracks and splits. Tar oils are best applied during hot weather when they are more fluid, or else, if they are viscous, they should be heated before use. Two coats give much better protection than one. Any second or subsequent coats should be applied after the first has dried off. Particularly thorough treatment should always be given to any exposed end grain as decay often starts there.

The ends of any timbers that have to be cut to size after they have received impregnation treatment should always be thoroughly brushed to protect any untreated wood in the core of the pieces that has been laid bare by cross cutting.

Brush treatment of wood that is freely exposed can be repeated at intervals of about three years, and it can confer lasting durability to such a structure; fence palings, for instance, may be preserved indefinitely in this way. On the other hand timber that is not accessible to repeated treatment, such as the underground portions of fence posts, cannot be effectively preserved by brushing. If the limitations of brush treatment were more widely understood there would be many fewer complaints about 'treated' timber having failed in service.

Spraying

Spraying is a convenient method for applying preservatives to any large areas, such as weather-boarding on houses. It is also used extensively for applying insecticides to roof timbers infected with woodworm, enabling operations to reach woodwork that is inaccessible to brush treatment. Fungicidal solutions can conveniently be sprayed on to walls infected with Dry Rot Fungus. For this method a nozzle designed to deliver a rather coarse spray should be used. Fine atomising sprays tend to waste

End view of small impregnating cylinder showing coils for heating creosote and bogey on rails

Quick locking door on end of impregnation cylinder

liquid in spray drifting away, and also to make the atmosphere in a confined space very unpleasant for the operatives. Respirators should always be provided for operatives applying chlorinated hydrocarbons or mineral oils in closed spaces; and the fire hazards involved must never be forgotten.

Dipping and Soaking

Total immersion of the pieces of wood to be treated in a bath of preservative is a more effective way of application than brushing or spraying, as it ensures that every portion of the surface is completely wetted. If the period of immersion is quite short the absorption obtained is similar to that achieved by brushing—a ten second dip gives roughly the same absorption as one brush coat, while soaking for ten minutes results in an uptake of preservative about the equivalent to that obtained with three brush applied coats. As with brushing it is the penetration along the grain from the exposed end grain which accounts for much of the absorption.

Short periods of immersion may give worthwhile protection to thin material consisting mainly of sapwood, such as packing case shooks, or seed boxes. For joinery such as window frames a three minute immersion in a clean solvent type preservative should be considered a minimum treatment, and ten minutes will give more reliable protection. Other factors which influence the final result are the nature of the preservative, and the degree to which it penetrates and distributes itself after treatment when the solvent has dried out.

It has recently been shown by Smith and Purslow that, after rapid absorption during the first ten seconds or so, the average penetration and the amount of preservative absorbed are proportional to the square root of the time of immersion.

Certain liquids continue to move into the wood for some time after the latter has been taken out of the fluid. Preservatives such as pentachlorophenol in a light solvent oil will continue to penetrate into the wood for a considerable time, thus reducing the effective concentration in the surface layers. Sodium pentachlorophenate in aqueous solution will penetrate much less deeply and so a higher concentration of the salt may be retained in the surface layers.

D

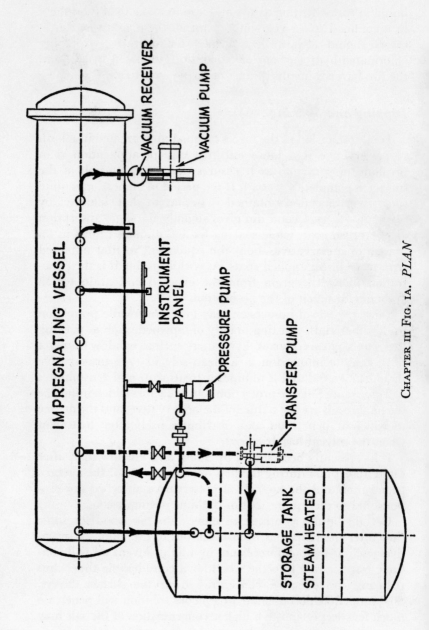

VACUUM RECEIVER

VACUUM PUMP

IMPREGNATING VESSEL

INSTRUMENT PANEL

PRESSURE PUMP

TRANSFER PUMP

STORAGE TANK
STEAM HEATED

Chapter III Fig. 1A. *PLAN*

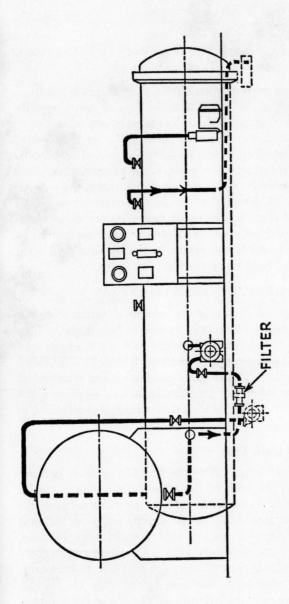

FILTER

CHAPTER III FIG 1B. *ELEVATION*
Diagrammatic arrangement of a pressure creosoting plant

Any specification for treatment of timber by short periods of immersion must take into consideration the following factors:

1. Species of Wood.
2. Nature of preservative, and of solvent, if any, to be used.
3. Geometrical shape of the pieces of wood.

The higher the proportion of end grain the quicker is the fluid absorbed. Rough sawn wood absorbs liquids more rapidly during the first five minutes than does planed wood.

Prolonged soaking, running into periods of a week or more, will result in quite deep penetration into seasoned softwoods. This method of treating fence posts, using pentachlorophenol in fuel oil, has been quite widely adopted on farms in the U.S.A., but has not been used to any extent in this country. Since the treating tanks are occupied for many days with one charge, the process can be used only where relatively small quantities of wood have to be treated, and generally the hot and cold open tank treatment is found more efficient. See below.

PRESSURE TREATMENTS

The penetration of preservatives into most timbers is slow and irregular if they are merely immersed in liquid, so the idea of applying a positive external pressure to force fluid into the pores of the wood was developed at an early date in the history of wood preservation. The original patent for the injection of oil into wood was taken out by John Bethell in 1838, and the general proceedure which he then described is still followed to this day.

Bethell, or Full Cell, Process

Bethell's process is often called the Full Cell Process because it results in filling the cells of the treated zone with a liquid. When impregnating wood with water-borne preservatives this process is almost invariably used. Briefly it is as follows: The seasoned timber is loaded into a stout steel cylinder which can be hermetically closed with a pressure door. In commercial treating plants the cylinders are 3 to 9 ft. in diameter, and their length may be as much as 150 ft. (See Pl. III, 1.) The timber is generally loaded onto small cars, or bogies, running on rails inside the cylinder. (See Pl. III, 2 and 3.) In

Standing pole being treated at ground level by Cobra method

6. Poles being treated by Cobra method prior to erection

7. Use of forester's increment borer to determine condition of pole. This is also used for determining depth of penetration of creosote

the original Bethell process a vacuum of about 22 ins. was drawn inside the cylinder, with the object of extracting as much of the air held in the cells of the wood as possible. Depending on the size of the timbers to be treated the vacuum is held for from 15 up to 60 minutes. The cylinder is then filled with the preservative and a pressure is applied to force the liquid into the wood. The final pressure attained is generally 150 to 175 lbs. sq. in. (See fig. 2.) If much higher pressures are applied to softwoods they may collapse.

After the required amount of preservative has been absorbed by the wood the pressure is released and the liquid drained from the cylinder. A short period of vacuum is finally applied to remove surplus liquid from the surface of the wood. Tar oil preservatives are generally heated, before they are pumped into

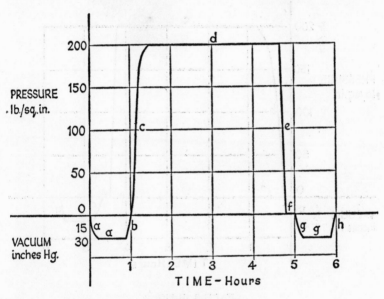

CHAPTER III FIG. 2

'Bethell' (Full Cell) System

a. Preliminary vacuum period
b. Fill cylinder with preservative
c. Build up pressure
d. Maximum pressure held
e. Release pressure

f. Empty cylinder of preservative
g. Final vacuum period
h. Release vacuum

the cylinder, to 175°-200°F depending on their viscosity. Aqueous solutions may also be heated to a certain degree as this facilitates penetration.

Empty Cell Process

This is another pressure method of applying tar oil preservatives which gives equally deep penetration but results in a lower final absorption of oil. This reduces the cost of the treatment, and also minimises the risk of the oil bleeding out from the impregnated timber after it is in use. In this method the preliminary vacuum is omitted and the oil is applied to the wood either at atmospheric pressure (*Lowry Process*), or after a preliminary air pressure has been applied (*Rueping Process*). (See

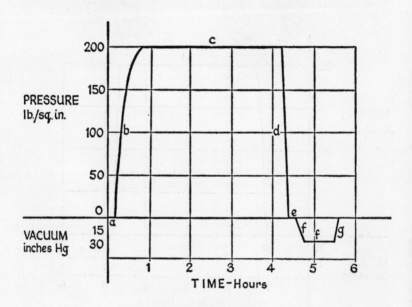

CHAPTER III FIG. 3

'Lowry' (Empty Cell) System

a. Fill cylinder with preservative at atmospheric pressure	*e.* Empty cylinder of preservative
b. Build up pressure	*f.* Final vacuum period
c. Maximum pressure held	*g.* Release vacuum
d. Release pressure	

Figs. 2 and 3.) In either case the air present in the wood becomes compressed so that when the oil pressure is released and the final vacuum is applied the compressed air in the cells expands again and drives out a proportion of the oil present in the cell spaces, leaving, of course, a film of oil on the walls of the cells.

The amount of preservative absorbed by the impregnated timber is measured by weighing the charge before and after impregnation. It is customary to express the degree of treatment in terms of weight of preservative absorbed per cubic unit of volume of wood, i.e. as lbs. per cubic ft. in English units, or Kgs. cub. metre in metric units. The average retentions obtained in commercial practice vary between 6 and 12 lbs. of fluid per

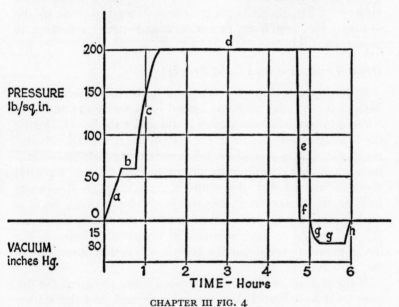

CHAPTER III FIG. 4

'Rueping' (Empty Cell) System

a. Preliminary air pressure applied
b. Fill cylinder with air pressure maintained
c. Build up pressure
d. Maximum pressure held
e. Release pressure
f. Empty cylinder of preservative
g. Final vacuum period
h. Release vacuum

cub. ft., depending on the species of wood and the size of the material being treated. Higher absorptions are required in thin material through which the preservative can penetrate completely than are necessary in large-sized timbers. Not only is it practically impossible to achieve complete impregnation of large baulks or poles, but it would be extravagant and quite unnecessary to attempt to do so. Provided there is a fully impregnated zone of adequate thickness on the exterior of a pole or timber infection cannot reach the untreated wood in the core, and this will therefore remain in a sound condition indefinitely.

The cost of the complete installation required for the pressure impregnation of timber in cylinders will amount to many thousands of pounds, since much ancillary equipment is required in addition to the cylinders, storage tanks and pumps. However for many purposes treatment in an open tank by the so-called Hot and Cold Process gives adequate protection to permeable timbers.

Open Tank, Hot and Cold Process

In this open tank process seasoned timber is submerged in a bath of preservative which is heated for a few hours and then allowed to cool while the timber is still under the liquid. During the heating period the air in the cells of the wood expands and much of it escapes as bubbles. When the timber cools down again the air remaining in the cells contracts, thus creating a partial vacuum, and the normal pressure of the atmosphere then tends to force the preservative into the pores of the wood. So it is during the cooling period that most of the absorption takes place. The greater the difference in temperature between the hot bath and the cold one the greater will be the absorption of the preservative.

If the volume of wood to be treated is not too great the fire may be drawn from below the treating tank and the timber allowed to cool for from 4 to 5 hours in the same tank in which it was heated. But if a greater output of treated wood is required the cooling part of the treatment may be given by quickly transferring the heated wood to another tank containing cold preservative, or by drawing out the hot liquid and replacing it instantly with cold.

When using creosote the temperature during heating should

not exceed 200°F, and great care must be taken not to boil creosote over an open fire as it will ignite if it overflows. When using a water-borne preservative the manufacturers' instructions regarding the safe maximum temperature must be observed, as some modern preservatives of this type will throw a deposit if overheated.

A simple modification of the open tank method is often used on farms and estates for treating the butt ends of posts. A stout steel drum of about 90 gallons capacity and measuring about 42 ins. high by 32 ins. wide, is placed on a rough hearth of bricks around a shallow hole in the ground, with a piece of three inch wide piping fixed at the back to ensure a good

CHAPTER III
FIG. 5

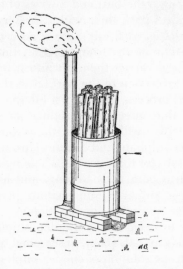

draught. (See Fig. 5.) The posts, which must be well seasoned, are stood vertically in the drum which is then filled two-thirds full with creosote. This is heated till it reaches about 200°F at which temperature it is held for an hour or so before the fire is extinguished to allow cooling to take place. As oil is absorbed during cooling it may be necessary to add more preservative to keep up the level, at the same time the exposed parts of the posts above the oil should be brushed over freely with preservative. Surprisingly good absorptions can often be obtained by butt treatment if the timber treated is round, well seasoned wood consisting mostly of sapwood.

DIFFUSION TREATMENTS

Diffusion treatments achieve deep penetration of water-borne preservatives by the gradual diffusion of the chemicals from a strong solution, or paste, applied, either to the surface of green unseasoned timber, or into holes made in the wood at points where there is the greatest risk of decay.

In order to get worthwhile penetration by diffusion of a preservative salt into wood it is essential that the timber should remain in a moist saturated condition for some time after the preservative has been applied in a concentrated form.

The simplest way to introduce a diffusible preservative into a post is to bore into the butt end a series of holes, $\frac{3}{4}$ to 1 inch in diameter, and to pack these with a preservative salt. They should then be plugged firmly with a cork or short piece of wooden dowel. As moisture from the soil enters the post it dissolves the salts and carries them up into it for some distance. Quite effective protection of the portion in the ground can be provided by this process, especially if alternate holes are filled with chemicals that interact to produce an insoluble salt, as then the preservative will persist in the wood for a long time. Probably copper sulphate and sodium chromate are the most suitable pair of salts for this purpose. These react to form copper chromate which is both toxic to fungi and highly resistant to leaching. Copper sulphate and sodium pentachlorophenate should also prove a suitable combination.

Another way to bring about the deposition of an insoluble salt in the wood is to soak green, unseasoned, peeled posts for a few days in a strong solution of copper sulphate, and to follow this by soaking them in a second solution containing a similar concentration of sodium chromate.

A novel method for achieving deep penetration of solvent type preservative by means of a single application of an emulsion has been described by Boocock (1960), who refers to it by the proprietary name of 'Woodtreat'. The preservative— e.g. pentachlorophenol—is applied as a thick gel-like, mayonnaise-type emulsion which sustains itself on the surface of the wood until the water evaporates and the oily material soaks into the wood. It is claimed that deep and uniform penetration into resistant timbers such as Douglas Fir can be achieved by this method, which should be particularly useful for in-situ treatment of infected timber in buildings.

Cobra Process

An ingenious way of introducing preservative salts into poles is that known as the Cobra Process. A preservative paste is injected into the wood through a hollow flat 'needle' or tooth, which is forced into the wood parallel to its grain to a depth of two inches or so, so that little damage is done to the wood and no appreciable weakening results. The injections are given to the zone just above and below the ground level where the risk of decay is greatest. From 80 to 100 injections may be given, depending on the size of the pole; and the quantity of salts used should be between $\frac{1}{2}$ and 1 lb. per pole. (See Pl. III, 6.)

This method is most commonly used for the treatment of standing poles that have begun to show signs of incipient decay at the ground line. Millions of poles have been treated in this way and it has been claimed that the average life of poles treated by the Cobra Process is extended by 15 to 20 years. The method is also used to provide additional protection in the vulnerable ground line area of poles of species, such as Spruce and Larch, in which pressure treatment is difficult. It can also conveniently be applied in remote and inaccesible regions where no facilities for impregnation exist.

Osmose Process

In the Osmose Process the green poles are brushed over with a thin layer of a preservative paste immediately after they have been barked. They are then closely piled, covered with a waterproof sheet to prevent their drying out, and left for about thirty days—or somewhat longer if the poles are of large size. After this time the preservative, which is generally a sodium fluoride dinitrophenol mixture, should have penetrated deeply into the wood, giving an absorption of $\frac{1}{4}$ to $\frac{1}{2}$ lb. of dry salts per cubic ft. of wood. Fence posts treated in this way are reported to have given good service in Canada and the U.S.A.

Bandage Process

A convenient way of applying a preservative locally to a vulnerable zone of a post at ground level is to attach tightly around it a quilted bandage containing, between the two layers of cloth, small quantities of preservative salts. The idea of this is that the moisture from the soil passing through the bandage will carry the salts into the wood.

Diffusion Treatments Involving Heat

Diffusion methods have been developed in Australia and New Zealand which involve dipping the green timber in a heated solution containing a mixture of borax and boric acid. The first of these methods, called the *Steaming-Cold Quench*, combines the principle of the hot and cold bath plus diffusion impregation. The timber is steamed at about 85°C for a few hours in a chamber rather like a timber drying kiln. This is then flooded with a cold 2-3% boric acid equivalent solution in which it is left for 12-14 hours. After this period the timber is removed from the treating chamber and then kept under restricted drying conditions for about two weeks. In 2-in. thick material penetration should then be complete.

A development from the above method was the use of much higher concentrations in the so-called *Hot immersion Treatment*. In this method the preservative enters the green timber by diffusion from a hot concentrated solution. It has been shown that the amount of chemical that enters the wood is directly proportional to the concentration of the solution and the square root of the immersion time, and inversely proportional to the thickness of the timber so that

$$\frac{\text{Concentration \% } \times \text{ Time}}{\text{\% Retention required } \times \text{ Thickness}} = \text{A constant}$$

If concentrations of 3 to 6% boric acid equivalent are used immersion times vary from two to four hours for 1-in. thick timber. If however much higher concentrations, up to 30-40%, can be used quite short periods of immersion are sufficient; or indeed the solution may even be sprayed onto the timber if the pieces are not too thick.

For further details regarding this method reference should be made to a paper by D. G. Carr (1959).

SAP-REPLACEMENT METHODS

The principle of this method is to fix to the butt end of a freshly felled pole a cap containing a solution of preservative.

Timber being treated by immersion in solvent-type preservative

Timber after immersion treatment. Piled so that excess fluid can
drain back into tank

The Boucherie method for treatment of poles by sap replacement with preservative

This cap is connected by a rubber tube to a reservoir at a much higher level, so that a hydrostatic pressure is exerted. Thus the liquid is slowly forced through the pores of the wood, and at the same time the sap is driven out at the top end of the pole. (See Pl. III, 9.) Treatment is continued until the solution appears at the top end. In this way excellent penetration of the sap wood can be achieved. In the original Boucherie process only copper sulphate was used for this treatment and somewhat variable results have been reported. It has recently been shown, however, that other modern improved formulations of salts that become more highly fixed in the wood can be applied in this way. This method is likely to be most economically advantageous in remote areas where impregnation facilities are lacking, and where the cost of labour is not too high.

It must be emphasised that the method of applying a preservative is quite as important as the nature of the preservative itself. Therefore any specification for treatment should set out clearly the method by which the preservative is to be applied, and what retention of preservative is to be achieved. Many failures and disappointments would be avoided if this were more generally recognised by architects and others. Merely to ask that timber should be 'creosoted' may result in only a single brush coat being applied, which for timber in contact with the ground would be practically useless. When specifying an impregnation treatment a minimum average retention of preservative per unit volume of the wood should be laid down. When specifying that timber shall be brushed with a preservative the number of coats to be applied should be stated, or a minimum quantity per unit of surface area specified. Similarly if timber is to be steeped a certain minimum period of immersion should be insisted on.

REFERENCES

Boocock, D. 'A New Technique for the Eradication of Timber Pests', *Pest Technology*, July 1960, p. 196.
Carr, D. G. 'Boron as a Timber Preservative', *Wood*, Sept./Oct./Nov./1958.
Smith, D. N., and Purslow. 'Preservative Treatment of Pine Sapwood', *Timber Technology*, **68**, p. 67, 1960.

CHAPTER IV

WOOD PRESERVATIVES

An astonishing variety of chemicals have been suggested over the years for the preservation of timber. As early as 1817 Chapman, the writer of a treatise on wood preservation, was complaining that:

'Almost every chemical principle or compound of any plausibility has been suggested in the course of the last five years, and submitted to the Admiralty or Navy Boards, but the multiplicity and contradiction of opinion forms nearly an inextricable labyrinth.'

Since then hundreds of different chemicals, many of them by-products of some industrial process, have been suggested, either singly or in combination, and the patent offices of the world contain innumerable descriptions of formulations for improved methods of treating wood. But of all this wide range of substances comparatively few have been found which are at the same time effective and devoid of objectionable properties.

Among the requirements of an effective wood preservative the following characteristics are the most important:

1. High toxicity towards wood destroying organisms.
2. Permanence in the treated wood.
3. Ability to penetrate deeply into wood.
4. Freedom from deleterious effects on the wood itself.
5. Non-corrosive to metals.
6. Without harmful effects on the operatives and those who handle the treated wood.

There is no one ideal preservative suitable for use on every kind of wood in every sort of situation. For any particular purpose the choice is often limited and sometimes there is only one that is wholly suitable for that particular job. So before deciding what preservative to apply thought must be given as to any special requirements imposed by the situation in which the treated wood will be used. For instance resistance of the preservative to leaching will be of the first importance on timber used in the open where it will be exposed to the rain. For timber to be used in the vicinity of food stuffs the absence of any odour will be essential. Where the fire risk is serious a non-flammable preservative that can be combined with a fire retardant is desirable—and so on.

Wood preservatives are commonly classified into three main groups:

1. Preservative oils derived from coal tar, petroleum or wood tar.
2. Water-borne chemicals.
3. Solvent type preservatives containing chemicals toxic to fungi and insects which are soluble only in organic solvents.

TAR OIL PRESERVATIVES

Creosote

For over 100 years creosote has been used successfully for the preservation of timber, and it has given such good results that for many people the terms 'wood preservation' and 'creosoting' are almost synonymous. From extensive service records kept by the Post Office and railways it is known that properly creosoted wooden poles and sleepers can withstand decay almost indefinitely. When failure does occur it can almost always be attributed either to faulty treatment, or to the wood having been insufficiently seasoned before treatment.

Coal tar creosote is by far the most important of the oil type wood preservatives, though there are other oils distilled from tars that have been used successfully for the purpose.

Creosote may be broadly defined as those fractions of the distillates from coal tar that boil between 200° and 400°C. It is a complicated mixture of a large number of organic compounds, and the relative proportions of these depend both on the composition of the original coal and the method by which it was carbonised.

The main constituents of creosote may be classified into:

1. Tar acids—phenol, cresol, xylenol, etc.
2. Tar bases—pyridine, quinolin and acridine.
3. 'Neutral' oils, consisting of a mixture of napthalene, anthracene, and other neutral hydrocarbons.

There has been much discussion and controversy as to the role that these various ingredients play in preserving wood. At one time it was thought that the tar acids, which are undoubtedly very toxic to fungi and insects, made an important contribution to the toxicity of the creosote as a whole. Later, when the effectiveness of the various constituents was tested against fungi in the laboratory, it became apparent that the so-called 'neutral' oils are themselves toxic to fungi, and that the extraction of the tar acids and bases does not appreciably reduce the preservative value of the creosote. It has also been shown that the tar acids disappear fairly quickly from treated wood as a result of evaporation, leaching and polymerisation, so there is no reason for demanding that they should be present in large amounts in the original oils.

A similar question about which there has been much discussion is the relative importance of the fractions that boil at various temperatures. Using the wood block method of testing it has been shown quite conclusively that the higher boiling fractions are in fact toxic to fungi. Nowadays the consensus of opinion seems to be that it is much better for the oil to contain a relatively high proportion of the heavier fractions that come over between 250° and 350°C, as these are the fractions that evaporate most slowly and which persist for the longest time in the wood. If the treated timber is to be exposed to severe weathering a heavy oil, rather than a light one, should be chosen, provided that it is not too viscous to penetrate deeply.

Since the viscosity of the oil decreases rapidly as the temperature rises it is highly desirable that creosote should be hot when it is applied to the timber. Any creosote that conforms to the specification drawn up by the British Standards Institute (B.S. No. 144) will give excellent and long lasting protection to timber in the open, provided that it is properly applied. Coal tar distillates (other than creosote to B.S. 144), which are primarily for use in the hot and cold process or by brush application, are covered in B.S. 3051, published in 1958.

Nearly all the experiments on the relative value of different kinds of creosote have been carried out on timber that has been impregnated under pressure. When the oil is to be applied by brushing or steeping it may be desirable to use a lighter, less viscous oil, or what might be called a 'multigrade' oil, containing both low and high boiling fractions. Alternatively an initial treatment might be given with a light penetrating oil, followed by one with a heavier oil, such as a mixture of creosote and tar, which would help to retain the lighter oil and provide some degree of weather resistance to the surface.

Some of the proprietary products prepared from creosote, especially those designed for interior use, contain a fairly high proportion of the lighter fractions which dry off quickly, leaving a clean surface. These interior grades are good floor stains and give a useful measure of protection, especially to thin material, but obviously they cannot be expected to give permanent protection to timber that is fully exposed to the weather. For this reason these interior grades should never be used for exterior woodwork. The exterior grades which contain a greater proportion of the higher boiling fractions give much more lasting protection.

The proprietary tar oil preservatives are generally cleaner than straight creosote, and may be obtained in a number of pleasing colours. By buying one of the well-known proprietary brands the purchaser can be sure of obtaining a tar oil preservative of consistent composition and high toxicity.

Other Tar Oil Preservatives

The tar produced by the low temperature carbonisation process used for the production of smokeless fuels differs in many respects from that produced by the ordinary high temperature carbonisation of coal. Similarly the oils distilled from these tars differ from creosote and tend to contain a much higher content of tar acids. Nevertheless these oils have given good results in both field and laboratory tests, and it is generally considered that they can be relied on to give effective and long lasting protection.

Wood tar, which is a by-product of the destructive distillation of wood, has long been used for the preservation of timber and cordage. It is undoubtedly very toxic to fungi, but it is variable in quality, and few attempts have been made to distil from it a creosote of uniform quality. Since only small quantities of wood tar are produced in this country no significant amount is available for wood preservation. Where it can be obtained at a reasonable price it can be used for the treatment of external

E

woodwork but its penetrating smell makes it unsuitable for interior use.

Petroleum distillates such as white spirit, kerosene, and diesel fuel oils are not by themselves toxic enough to make good preservatives but they are often used as solvents for other more toxic materials. Their use for this purpose will be discussed on page 62.

Mixtures of creosote and fuel oil have often been used for the impregnation of railway sleepers in countries where the petroleum products are cheaper than creosote, and they have been found to give very satisfactory protection. The formation of a heavy sludge on mixing petroleum products with creosote often causes trouble, and so preliminary experiments should always be made to determine the degree of sludging likely to occur. Heavy aromatic petroleums are said to be the most suitable for making such mixtures.

Reasons for Using Tar Oil Preservatives

Among the many advantages that tar oil preservatives possess the following should especially be borne in mind:

1. Their effectiveness against both fungal decay and insect attack, when properly applied, is fully established and well recognised.
2. The penetration and retentions required for various kinds of wood, and to timber of different dimensions, are well known through practical experience.
3. They tend to reduce the risk of splitting and surface checking and therefore are particularly valuable for the preservation of railway sleepers.
4. They are available in large quantities in most parts of the country, and in the United Kingdom they are relatively cheap.
5. Standard specifications exist both for the liquids themselves and for the treating procedures and requirements.
6. They confer a pleasing colour to the treated wood.
7. They are not usually corrosive to metals.
8. They can easily be applied by brushing, spraying, or steeping in cases where only superficial applications are considered necessary.

Choice of Method of Application

It is generally agreed that when using tar oils for any of the following purposes some form of impregnation process, either in a pressure cylinder or by the hot and cold open tank method, is essential:

1. All timber that is to be in contact with the ground, e.g. poles, sleepers and fence posts.
2. Timbers that are to be embedded in concrete or in close contact with concrete that touches the ground, e.g. fixing battens for floor boards.
3. Timbers for marine work.

Surface application of a suitable grade of creosote by thorough brushing or spraying will give a fair degree of protection to thin material which is not in contact with the soil, such as weather boarding and palings. It is also a convenient way of treating small portable articles such as wheelbarrows, chicken houses, and so on, which can be retreated by further applications after a certain number of years. If green algae, mosses or lichens appear on the surface of the wood a fresh application of preservative is obviously called for. Brush treatments are best undertaken out of doors during the summer when the wood is in a dry condition and the oil less viscous than it is in winter.

Wall plates and the ends of joists and rafters are often brushed with creosote before being built into a house. This certainly gives them some protection against infection during the critical period when there is still moisture in the new brickwork; but such superficial treatment cannot be relied on to give really permanent protection, especially as it is impossible to repeat the treatment on such timbers, which once built into the walls are inaccessible.

Disadvantages of Tar Oil Preservatives

1. All tar oils are partially volatile and give off pungent, though not necessarily objectionable, odours. This means that they should never be used where there may be a risk of the fumes contaminating foodstuffs such as fruit or dairy produce, or in a shop such as a pharmacy or perfumery where any strange odours would be undesirable. Nor should tar oils be used in greenhouses or on seed boxes

as the volatile fractions of creosote are poisonous to plants. Creosote has been used, after dilution with petrol, for treating bed boards in mushroom houses, but if the beds are spawned soon after this treatment there may be a risk of damage to the ensuing crop.

2. Creosote oils tend to bleed from impregnated timber especially when the latter is exposed to sunshine, and then the surface of the wood may become sticky and will soil any clothing with which it may come in contact.

3. Paint cannot normally be applied to creosoted wood.

Over the years a certain amount of creosote is lost by evaporation from the surface layers. The rate of such loss from any given piece of wood must obviously depend on the geometrical shape of the piece, or, in other words, on the ratio of the surface area to the volume. In impregnated solid timber, such as a pole or a joist, the loss of creosote from the surface of the wood is made good by the slow movement of oil from the reserves in the deeper layers. In plywood, however, there is not sufficient thickness to contain such a reserve of oil, and from field tests there are indications that creosote cannot protect plywood for such long periods as solid timber.

Tar Oils and Fire Hazards

It used to be thought that the creosoting of wood increased its flammability, but such is not the case—except for quite a short time after impregnation, while the surface layers still contain some of the more volatile fractions. In fact authorities are now generally agreed that it is actually more difficult to ignite creosoted wood than untreated wood, though once a fire is established and burning strongly, creosoted timber will burn more fiercely, and give off more smoke, than will untreated timber.

Emulsions of Tar Oils

At one time there was considerable interest in the use of emulsions of water soluble preservatives with tar oils. It was hoped that these would combine the advantages of both types and that the addition of the oil would reduce the leaching of the salts. However the development of highly fixed water-borne preservatives has reduced interest in this aspect of emulsions and at the present time, as far as the author knows, no emulsions of creosote are being used for wood preservation in this country.

Sources of Information on Tar Oils

A great deal of information about creosote and how it should be used can be found in such standard works on wood preservation as *Wood Preservation* by Hunt and Garret, 2nd edition 1958, and *Holzkonservierung* by Mahlke-Troschel-Liese.

Volume I of *Conservacion de Maderas en Sus Aspectos Teorico Industrial y Economico*, 1952, by J. Benito Martinez, is probably the most exhaustive book on tar oil preservatives. It runs to some 550 pages and contains many illustrations and a very full bibliography.

Research on tar oils is carried out in the laboratories of the Coal Tar Research Association at Gomersal, near Leeds. Problems relating to their use are dealt with by the Association of Tar Distillers.

WATER-BORNE PRESERVATIVES

At one time it was usual to call preservatives that were applied in aqueous solutions 'water soluble', but as this term suggests that they remain soluble in water it is now customary to refer to them as 'water-borne'. This implies only that they are borne, or carried, into the wood as aqueous solutions and is therefore a more accurate description.

Metallic salts dissolved in water were among the first substances to be used for the preservation of wood. Kyan's patent for the use of mercuric chloride as a preservative was granted in 1832, and the method for treating green timber with copper sulphate was patented by Boucherie in 1838. But none of the earlier formulations of water soluble materials became fixed in the wood to any appreciable degree, and therefore the salts were liable to be 'leached' (washed) out if exposed to rain for any length of time, or to diffuse out if left for long periods in contact with water, soil or other damp material. As many of the major uses for preserved timber involved exposure to weather and contact with the soil, there was naturally only limited interest in this type of preservative. They were also usually rated rather low, in comparison with tar oil products, in field tests, in which posts, treated with various preservatives, were set in the ground, and their 'life' compared with that of untreated wood.

Then came the discovery that the addition of chromates to mixtures of certain metallic salts rendered them more or less insoluble in the wood. This greatly extended their field of application, but, as some of the earlier formulations incorporating chromates did not give such lasting protection as the manufacturers had hoped and predicted, some disappointments ensued, the shadows of which still darken the reputation of certain water-borne preservatives. Nevertheless the best of the more recently developed formulations do now achieve almost complete fixation of the salts in the wood, and, if properly applied, they will give lasting protection to timber, even under severe conditions of exposure.

Parallel with these developments there has been growing the realisation that much woodwork, even if it is not fully exposed to the weather, as for example in buildings and mines, nevertheless requires treatment in order to protect it against insect and fungal attack. As in such situations there is little risk of leaching, a water-borne preservative, despite not being wholly or even partially fixed in the wood, may give longlasting and adequate protection.

Many different water soluble chemicals have been used for wood preservation, either singly or in combination, many of them being by-products not specifically manufactured for this purpose. It would be tedious and unprofitable to list them all, and so in the following pages only those products that are in commercial use to-day will be considered.

Advantages of Water-Borne Preservatives

1. They can be transported in solid, or concentrated form and made up in the place where they are to be used with the cheapest of all solvents—water. This makes their use particularly economical in places where transport charges are high, and where there are no natural sources of oil.
2. Formulations of water-borne chemicals that are equally effective against both fungi and insects can easily be prepared.

3. They leave the wood in a clean condition which is not unpleasant to handle.
4. The treated wood can be painted over once the water has dried off.
5. They are usually odourless.
6. They can readily be combined with fire retardant chemicals.

Disadvantages of Water-Borne Preservatives

The principal disadvantage of this type of preservative is that when applied to seasoned timber it rewets the wood and thereby causes it to swell. Such dimensional changes may lead to distortion of parts machined to fine limits. It is therefore necessary to re-dry the treated wood after impregnation before using it in any place where shrinkage would be objectionable.

Classification of Water-Borne Preservatives

Water-borne preservatives may conveniently be classified into four groups:

A. Those intended for the impregnation of structural timber for outdoor use.
B. Those intended for treating green or wet timber by steeping, or by a diffusion method such as the Osmose or Cobra process.
C. Those intended for use in the sap-replacement method, commonly known as the Boucherie treatment.
D. Those intended for surface application to existing timber in buildings, or to thin material such as packing cases.

A. Water-Borne Preservatives for External Use. To-day most water-borne preservatives intended for external use contain an appreciable percentage of an alkaline chromate, which serves to 'fix' the other chemicals and render them less liable to leach out. The earlier mixtures of this type—often referred to in Germany as U. Salts—contained sodium fluoride and dinitrophenol in addition to the chromate. These did not achieve a very high degree of fixation, but later it was found that when arsenical compounds were included they then gave quite good protection. Under severe conditions, however, even these, now known as U.A. Salts, failed to give complete and permanent protection to timbers that were in contact with the soil and exposed to attack by the microfungi that bring about Soft Rot.

The most prolonged and effective protection has been achieved by the use of carefully balanced mixtures of copper and chromium slats, with, or without, the addition of arsenic which enhances the toxicity of the mixture against insects. Celcure A, Tanalith C and Boliden K 33 are well-known preservatives of this latter type. Wood impregnated with adequate loadings of copper-chrome-arsenic mixtures has been shown to remain unaffected by fungal decay or insect attack over long periods, even under very severe conditions of exposure. The copper appears to contribute greatly to the effectiveness of the preservatives against the cellulose-destroying micro-fungi that cause Soft Rot. Copper-chrome preservatives have been used successfully for the treatment of the slats in water-cooling towers where the treated wood is exposed to the most severe and continuous leaching, and to Soft Rot organisms.

British Standards for Copper/Chrome, and Fluoride/Arsenate Chromate/Dinitrophenol wood preservatives have been prepared. In these the composition of the preservatives and the methods recommended for their application and analysis are set out. The minimum net retentions of dry salts required for timber in various situations are indicated in an Appendix. The minimum retentions generally specified are: $\frac{1}{2}$ lb./cub. ft. of Cu/Cr, and $\frac{1}{4}$-$\frac{1}{2}$ lb./cub. ft. of the F/As/Cr/DNP preservatives.

The use of zinc chloride solutions, formerly used in the Burnettising process, for the impregnation of timber, is now falling into disuse, due to the discovery of more toxic and permanent solutions; though chromated zinc chloride, which is more highly fixed in the wood, is still used on a fairly large scale in the U.S.A.

B. Salts for Diffusion Treatments. Salts intended for diffusion treatment of moist timber must either be applied in a highly concentrated solution, or else be mixed with some suitable binder to form a slurry, or paste, that will adhere to the wood while diffusion is taking place. They can also be applied on some form of bandage that can be fixed tightly to the wood. They must obviously be capable of relatively rapid diffusion into the substance of the wood at normal temperatures.

The mixture generally used in the Cobra treatments (see

p. 45) is composed of sodium fluoride, dinitrophenates and arsenates. The retentions of dry salts recommended are $\frac{1}{4}$-$\frac{1}{2}$ lb./ cub. ft. of wood treated.

Diffusion treatments have been very successfully employed for the application of boron solutions. The treatment of green veneers of timber with solutions of boric acid, before manufacture into plywood, in order to protect the plywood against *Lyctus* attack, was successfully used in Australia before the second World War. More recently mixtures of borax and boric acid for diffusion treatment of freshly sawn green timber have been developed in New Zealand. These boron compounds are highly toxic to wood-rotting fungi and to wood borers such as *Lyctus* and *Anobium*. In order to get a highly concentrated solution of approximately neutral reaction a mixture of one part of boric acid with 1·54 parts of decahydrate borax (or 1.18 parts of pentahydrate borax) is recommended. Solutions of this mixture can be obtained which, at a slightly elevated temperature (about 105°F) will contain approximately 30% boric acid equivalent. As explained on page 46 the concentration should be adjusted according to the thickness of the timber and the length of the period of immersion. Solutions containing 8-9% boric acid equivalent are commonly used when the timber is to be steeped for some time, while 25 to 40% solutions are used when the wood is only dipped momentarily, or when it is sprayed with the solution.

The average retention of boron salts recommended for protection of building timber is 1·25% boric acid equivalent based on the dry weight of the wood. This will usually result in an average concentration of 0·6% in the core of the treated pieces of wood, which is more than sufficient to protect susceptible timber against woodworm and the Dry Rot Fungus.

It has recently been shown by Griffiths and Cockcroft* that the concentration of boron in wood can rapidly be determined to an accuracy of ± 0.3% by making measurements in a reactor, of the neutron absorption of the treated wood, the nucleus of the boron atom having an amazing affinity for neutrons. Further work will be necessary before a laboratory bench method can be developed to deal with the routine analysis of many small samples, but the development of a non-destructive

* *J. Inst. Wood Sci.*, **7**, p. 73, 1961.

method for the accurate estimation of a preservative in wood is a major advance.

It has not yet been found possible to treat timber by diffusion processes with salts that become highly fixed in the wood. Therefore, so far as sawn timber is concerned, this method is more suitable for materials that are to be used in buildings than it is for external woodwork.

Injection by the Cobra process will arrest decay in standing poles which were not properly treated before erection, and thus will considerably prolong their life.

C. Salts for use in Sap Replacement Treatments. Copper sulphate at about 1% solution was used almost exclusively in the original Boucherie method of treating poles. Many thousands of poles have been treated in this way in Europe, but the protection given by the treatment has been rather erratic. An average service life of 11 to 14 years has been quoted, but there have also been reports of premature failures. A possible explanation of these failures is that they have occurred when the wood has been attacked by a fungus that is resistant to copper fungicides. Though copper solutions are exceedingly toxic to the spores of certain fungi, such as the Potato Blight Fungus, there are some wood-rotting species, especially certain *Poria* spp., that can tolerate quite high concentrations of copper. To-day copper sulphate is generally used for pressure impregnation only in combination with chromates. See page 58.

There are other water-borne preservatives which can be used in the Boucherie process. Tanalith C, for instance, has proved to be very suitable and should give much better protection than copper sulphate. Some salts that become fixed in the wood are not suitable because as they become precipitated in the wood they tend to choke up the vessels along which the liquid must pass.

D. Solutions for Surface Treatment. Any solution that is to be applied superficially by brushing or spraying must be highly toxic to wood-destroying fungi, and, if it is to give worthwhile and long lasting protection, it must also be nonvolatile. For timber that is already in position in a building or a ship there is no alternative to superficial treatment, though this may be supplemented by local injection of liquids, or by the insertion of pellets of solid preservatives.

In the past solutions of sodium fluoride, or of magnesium fluosilicate (silico-fluoride), at a strength of 6 to 8 oz. respectively, to the gallon of water, were widely used for the treatment of timber in buildings that had been affected by dry rot. In Germany a great variety of such fluoride and fluosilicate preparations have been used under many different proprietary names. While these products are undoubtedly toxic to fungi and insects there is evidence that the effectiveness of some of them is reduced after contact with lime or concrete. They are therefore not very suitable for sterilising walls built with lime mortar which has been permeated with the strands of the Dry Rot Fungus—*Merulius lacrymans*.

In this country to-day there are several proprietary water soluble wood preservatives that are intended for surface application. Some of the most effective of these are aqueous solutions of sodium pentachlorophenate, containing not less than 5% of this compound. It should be noted that the standard name recommended in B.S. 2474 for this chemical is sodium pentachlorophenoxide, but the older name is used in this book as it is so much better known. Pentachlorophenate applied in aqueous solution appears to persist for very much longer in the surface layers than do solutions of pentachlorophenol in light oily solvents, which tend to diffuse more deeply into the wood.

Situations Particularly Suitable for Water-Borne Preservatives

Although there are many situations in which the choice between one preservative and another will probably be made on the grounds of price, there are certain uses for which water-borne preservatives are particularly well suited.
These include:

1. Mining timbers.
2. Timbers for buildings in which any odours are undesirable e.g. linings of cold stores and refrigerated ships.
3. Woodwork that has subsequently to be painted.
4. The in-situ treatment of timber in buildings where there is the risk of staining plaster or paintwork.

One outstanding advantage of these preservatives is that their use can never involve any increased fire hazard, and they can therefore be sprayed in confined spaces without taking any special precautions to avoid naked lights or electric sparks. In fact they can readily be combined with fire-retardant salts (see Chapter XIII) to give a product having both preservative and fire-resistant properties.

SOLVENT TYPE PRESERVATIVES

In comparison with the tar oil and the water-borne preservatives the solvent types are, relatively speaking, newcomers. There is, therefore, less practical experience of their use, and fewer service records are available of their performance under practical conditions.

One may define a solvent type preservative as one consisting of a toxic substance, or substances, dissolved in a solvent other than water. Quite a wide range of substances have been suggested and used as the toxic ingredients, and a variety of solvents have been employed. Many of the more recent formulations include a mixture of toxic materials specifically intended to give protection against both fungi and insects. The composition of many of the well-known proprietary brands has been changed from time to time as new materials have become available, so that it is difficult for the purchaser to know exactly what materials he is using when he buys these products. The results of official tests carried out in the past may no longer be relevant if the composition has been changed in the meantime. Generally it is not easy for the user to make up his own solutions of this type, and even if he does succeed in getting the substance into solution the resulting product may not be as satisfactory as a proprietary one, which has been carefully formulated to prevent subsequent 'blooming' (crystalisation out) of the substance on the surface of the treated wood.

Chemicals Used

So far as this country is concerned there are comparatively few toxic chemicals in general use in solvent type wood preservatives. It is important in this connection to distinguish between fluids that are intended as preservatives against subsequent infection, and insecticides and fungicides that are primarily designed to kill organisms already present in the wood. Many of the latter type do, however, contain materials that persist in the wood and afford it some measure of protection against re-infestation.

The chemicals which have been used most extensively by British manufacturers of solvent type preservatives include chlorinated naphthalenes, metallic naphthenates, and pentachlorophenol. A very useful survey of the principal substances used in the formulation of solvent type preservatives is given in a series of articles in the journal *Pest Technology*, vol. 3.

For in-situ treatment of timber affected by wood boring insects it has become a common practice to reinforce the insecticidal properties of these preservatives by the addition of a potent insecticide such as benzene hexachloride or dieldrin.

Chlorinated Naphthalenes. Monochloronaphthalene is highly toxic to fungi and insects and, in its undiluted form, has been used for many years past in Germany where it is reported to have given excellent protection over long periods. In this country it has generally been employed as one of the ingredients dissolved in a light petroleum solvent. Precise information about its long term persistence when applied in this way is lacking.

The more highly chlorinated naphthalenes are waxy solids with a fairly high melting point. Halowax is the proprietary name of one such product which is manufactured and sold in the U.S.A. by Koppers Inc. Seekay Wax is the brand name for the chlorinated naphthalene manufactured by I.C.I. in the United Kingdom. These waxes are good insecticides and persist in the wood and they are included in a number of solvent type preservatives. They are appreciably more toxic to man and animals than monochloronaphthalene, and possible hazards arising during their formulation and application must be closely watched.

Naphthenates of zinc and copper have long been used for the preservation of textiles, cordage and timber. The copper compound is appreciably more toxic to fungi than the corresponding zinc one, and is generally to be preferred for use on wood. It does not leach out and, if present in adequate quantity, can give long lasting protection. Its copper content also renders it particularly effective against the cellulose destroying microfungi that destroy textiles. Copper naphthenate is not highly toxic to fungi and therefore strong solutions should always be used (i.e. containing about 6-8% of copper calculated as the metal), and the solution should be applied generously. Otherwise there is a possibility that the concentration in the surface layers of the wood may not be high enough to prevent attack by copper tolerant fungi such as species of *Poria*. Copper naphthenate solutions have been used with conspicuous success for the preservation of horticultural woodwork such as greenhouses and seed boxes, for which purpose they are particularly suitable as this chemical has no deleterious effect on plant life. Mercury naphthenates are reported to have given excellent protection against fungi and insects in several field tests, but their use has not become general.

Compounds of copper with fatty acids—e.g. the oleate, linoleate, and stearate compounds—do not seem as effective as copper naphthenate. Apparently the naphthenic acid itself contributes to the preservative qualities of the compound.

Pentachlorophenol. This chemical has exceptionally high toxicity to fungi, as was discovered during a search for chemicals that would prevent the growth of sapstain fungi on freshly sawn timber. Its sodium salt is now the most generally used fungicide for this purpose. Field tests of stakes impregnated with 5% pentachlorophenol in fuel oil have shown that it can give excellent and long lasting protection when applied in this particular solvent. However in this country where we have plentiful supplies of good creosote there has been little interest in using it in this way, and it is generally applied in a light mineral oil that will dry off and leave a clean surface. There is some evidence that its persistence in wood depends to a considerable extent on the particular solvent, and on the anti-blooming agent used in its formulation. If applied in a light solvent with an inadequate anti-blooming agent the chemical may crystalise out on the surface, and in the course of years it may disappear by slow volatilisation. Correct formulation and the use of really adequate amounts are essential in order to get the best results, and it cannot be recommended that the ordinary user should prepare his own solutions of pentachlorophenol from the pure chemical.

Copper Pentachlorophenate. Copper PCP is more toxic to fungi and also more persistent than PCP itself. It is only fairly recently that this compound has been used in wood preservation, but the results so far obtained are most promising and it will probably find much wider application in the future. It has been used with success for the preservation of wall boards against decay.

Benzene Hexachloride. BHC is the accepted B.S.I. common name of benzene hexachloride. The crude product contains several isomers of which the gamma one is by far the most effective. The name Lindane is often given to a product containing not less than 99% of the gamma isomer. BHC has been used with conspicuous success for treating logs against attack by Ambrosia Beetles using concentrations of about 0·75% gamma BHC. It persists surprisingly well and it has been found, for instance, that a ten second dip in 0·5% gamma BHC emulsion can give protection against *Lyctus* for as long as three years.

BHC is less toxic to man than most of the chlorinated insecticides and its use does not necessitate the wearing of protective clothing, though the use of a mask when spraying in confined spaces is recommended.

Dieldrin. Dieldrin is a very potent insecticide of the highly chlorinated hydrocarbon type made by Shell Chemicals Ltd., which acts as both a stomach and contact poison. It is very stable, insoluble in water and practically non-volatile so it persists extremely well in wood. It is effective against all the common wood borers at low concentrations. It has been used with success for ridding the soil around and below buildings of termites. It is toxic to mammals, and operatives who are regularly engaged in its manufacture and application should wear protective clothing. Masks should be worn by anyone spraying insecticides containing dieldrin in confined places.

Methods of Application

Since relatively expensive solvents are used in the preparation of this class of preservative, treatment becomes extremely expensive if high absorptions are to be obtained—unless the solvent can be recovered and used again and again. An impregnation treatment that permits the recovery of the solvent has been operated experimentally in the United States but has not been developed commercially in this country. Solvent type preservatives are therefore always applied by brushing, spraying or dipping, and the absorptions obtained naturally vary considerably according to the kind of wood, the dimensions and shape of the material being treated, as well as on the viscosity of the preservative itself. In these circumstances it is not surprising that somewhat variable results are reported as to the efficacy of these treatments. Ten minutes immersion or two flowing brushed-on coats may give really lasting protection to thin boarding consisting mainly of sapwood, as in seed boxes, but may be quite insufficient to protect large-sized members of less permeable woods.

It becomes even more difficult to specify suitable treatments when the material to be treated consists of pieces of various shapes, with differing amounts of sapwood and of end grain. A certain amount of experimentation should be carried out under practical conditions to arrive at a satisfactory treating schedule which will ensure adequate penetration. However toxic and effective a preservative may be it cannot give long lasting protection unless it penetrates for a certain depth into the wood. If only a thin superficial layer of wood is treated there will always be the risk that this will be damaged, thus opening ports of entry for rotting organisms. Also some slow loss of an organic preservative from the surface must inevitably occur, and to compensate for this there must either be a reserve of preservative within the wood, or the wood must be re-treated at intervals. Roofing shingles are one example of wood that should receive repeated treatments if indefinitely long protection is required.

For the treatment of timber in buildings where there have already been outbreaks of dry rot or woodworm, ten minutes steeping of the new timber used for replacements, and two full flowing brushed-on coats for the timber in situ, should be considered a minimum treatment with most solvent type preservatives.

It is false economy to apply a preservative so thinly that it does not adequately protect the wood. Unless really effective protection is given the treatment will be just a waste of time and materials.

Advantages of Solvent Type Preservatives

1. They do not cause swelling or distortion of the wood, as they contain no water, nor do they raise the grain of a planed surface.

2. They leave the wood in a clean condition—provided that a suitable solvent has been used—ready to receive paint after the solvent has evaporated.
3. They do not leach out of the wood if it is subsequently exposed to rain, as the toxic materials are generally insoluble in water.
4. They penetate well into any permeable timber.
5. They can be obtained either coloured or colourless, as required.

Disadvantages of Solvent Type Preservatives

One of the principal obstacles to the wider use of these preservatives in the United Kingdom is their relatively high cost, which reflects, of course, the cost of the solvents they contain. In counties where petroleum products are cheaper their price can be more competitive.

Another disadvantage is the increased flammability of the wood for a short time after the preservative has been applied. However this risk rapidly diminishes as the volatile solvent evaporates, since the other ingredients are not in themselves flammable. Investigations at the Fire Research Organisation indicate that 48 hours after a superficial treatment of all surfaces with a preservative dissolved in white spirit, the solvent normally has dried off, leaving a safe residue—provided that all the doors and windows have been left open. (See Fire Protection Association Technical Information Sheet, No. 3008, 'Fire Hazards of Wood Preservatives'.)

Uses for Solvent Type Preservatives

These preservatives are generally employed for specialised uses, for which, very often, they are specifically formulated. Among the most important uses are:

1. In-situ treatment of timber in buildings.
2. Preservation of horticultural timbers, such as greenhouses, garden furniture, seed boxes, etc.
3. Preservation of packing cases, especially those for military use, such as ammunition boxes.
4. Preservation of boat timbers which must be treated after fashioning to their final size on the job.
5. Preservation of wooden parts of vehicles, e.g. framing and floor boards of lorries, buses and caravans.

F

It must be emphasised that the choice of wood preservatives should only be made after due consideration of the purpose for which it is required. These considerations should include:

(a) the kind of wood to be treated and the dimensions and state of seasoning of the pieces;
(b) the methods available for applying the preservative; and
(c) the nature of the structure to be protected, and the uses to which it will be put, including any special hazards such as fungus, insects, or fire, to which it may be exposed.

The final decision must of course be influenced by the relative prices of the commercial products available in the particular country. In considering this the purchaser should make sure that proprietary products do, in fact, conform to the required specifications. It is easy enough to sell a product more cheaply if it contains less of the expensive active ingredients.

REFERENCE

Van Groenou, H. B., Rischen, H. W. L., and van den Berge, J. *Wood Preservation during the last Fifty Years* (Leiden 1951) contains much useful information about a wide range of preservatives, including many that are now only of historical interest.

CHAPTER V

EVALUATION OF WOOD PRESERVATIVES

Service Records

The value of a preservative cannot be said to be definitely proved until, after the lapse of a considerable time, it can be shown that some treated material has, in fact, lasted much longer than similar untreated material. As the untreated timber will itself endure for quite a few years, and the life of the treated timber may extend into several decades, it may be a very long time indeed before practical results can be shown. There is no doubt that this difficulty has seriously retarded the introduction of new and improved wood preservatives, as there has been a natural reluctance to use processes for which no service records can be produced; and until recently the evidence of accelerated laboratory tests has been regarded with scepticism.

Accurate records of the service life and performance of tele-graph poles impregnated with creosote have been kept by the postal authorities in this and other countries. Similar statistics relating to the track life of railway sleepers have been collected in a number of countries, and in the U.S.A. the American Wood Preservers Association has amassed a large amount of valuable data. As a result of all this work we can now predict, with a considerable degree of accuracy, the increase in the service life that any specified creosoting treatment will give to particular species of wood. Conditions vary so greatly from one locality to another in relation to the severity of fungal, weather, and soil conditions, that it is only possible to get an overall picture when accurate service records have become available from a wide range of sites.

Field Tests

The effectiveness of preservative treatments can be compared, from service data, only when a great deal of information from a wide range of sites is available. Deliberately planned experi-ments can be laid down, but to compare, for example, the effectiveness of creosote and creosote-petroleum mixtures, for the preservation of railway sleepers, would involve the controlled impregnation of many hundreds of sleepers, laid in various regions of higher and lower rainfall, in various types of ballast, and under varying conditions of traffic density. Such experiments involve considerable organisation, and many years must elapse before significant results are obtainable.

While the final proof of the suitability of a preservative treatment for any type of structure must ultimately be assessed by full scale service trials, a very great deal of information can be obtained from well designed field and laboratory tests, so that only those products that have every chance of being successful will be used for the final service trials.

The type of field test that has been used most generally is that known as 'the graveyard test'. In these experiments square billets of a perishable timber are impregnated with carefully measured quantities of the preservative under test. The test pieces may be thin round poles consisting mainly of sapwood, or they may be square billets measuring $24'' \times 4'' \times 2''$, or $24'' \times 2'' \times 2''$. These are embedded in the soil to a depth of six inches or so, and are examined at yearly intervals until they fail when struck with a hammer of a known weight. Untreated samples cut from the same piece of wood are set in the ground alongside the treated specimens and their lives (i.e. number of years before failure occurs) are compared. (See Pl. V, 1.) It is not necessary to wait until all the treated specimens have failed before estimating the average life, as from past experience it is possible to form a fairly accurate idea of the average life when only a proportion, say half the specimens, have rotted to the point of failure. Nevertheless it is necessary to wait for many years before useful comparisons can be made between reasonably effective preservatives. Only those that have little or no value will fail within the first five to ten years. Somewhat more rapid results can be obtained by reducing the size of the test pieces, but with very small stakes the surface to volume ratio is so much increased that when using creosote, or other tar oils which tend to evaporate from the surface of the wood, the results become less closely related to practice.

In the graveyard type of test the treated specimens are exposed to all the weathering influences, rain, sun and wind, which tend to wash out and evaporate preservatives, and there-

Field testing of preservative. Examining in the 'graveyard' an untreated specimen which has failed (*Crown copyright*)

fore it reflects fairly accurately the behaviour of a preservative used in a fence post, or a telegraph pole, set in the ground. It may, however, give a completely wrong impression as to the value of a water-borne preservative intended for use under cover in a building or mine. Treatments with fluorides or borates, for instance, give very poor results in soil burial tests in the open, though they are known to afford excellent protection to building and mining timbers which are not exposed to the leaching action of rain.

Laboratory Tests

In order to asess the potential value as wood preservatives of newly discovered fungicides and insecticides, and to compare them with the well established preservatives, efforts have been made to devise reliable laboratory methods of assay.

The principal factors that determine the effectiveness of a preservative are:

1. Toxicity to fungi and insects.
2. Permanence—i.e. no tendency to evaporate; and, for exposed woodwork, high resistance to leaching.
3. Ability to penetrate into wood.

There are other desirable qualities which can be assessed by means of laboratory tests, such as freedom from deleterious effects on the wood itself and from corrosive effects on metal fastenings. The effects of any treatment on the flammability of the wood can also be assessed fairly accurately in the laboratory.

Toxicity Tests against Fungi

Fungi vary enormously in their response to toxic chemicals. Some fungi can tolerate surprisingly high concentrations of certain preservatives which will inhibit other fungi at quite low concentrations. For instance some species of *Poria* will tolerate concentrations of copper salts fifty times greater than that required to kill *Lentinus lepidus*, which fungus, on the other hand, is much more resistant to creosote than are the *Poria* species. The implications of this wide variation in tolerance to poisons are that it is absolutely essential to use more than one test fungus when carrying out laboratory estimations of toxicity, and to choose as test organisms those species that are known to be tolerant of the chemical under test. For instance when testing a preservative based on copper, a *Poria* should certainly be included among the test fungi.

Agar Test. Over fifty years ago estimations of the toxicity of various fungicides to wood-rotting fungi were made by the so-called 'agar test'. In this test the amount of the chemical (dissolved or dispersed in a nutritive agar jelly) that will inhibit the growth of a pure culture of certain test fungi is determined by the following experiments: A graded series of concentrations are inoculated with little squares of mycelium cut from another culture. The petri dishes containing these various concentrations are then incubated for from two to four weeks, and the concentration above which no growth occurs is noted.

In the U.S.A. the technique for carrying out this test was refined until very precise results could be obtained. But investigators, especially in Europe, began to ask themselves what the results really signified in terms of wood-preserving power. An agar jelly is so different from a piece of wood, both chemically and physically, that it is difficult to relate results obtained in agar to what is likely to happen in wood. To give a simple example: impregnation of timber with waterproof wax might greatly increase its durability although the wax showed little toxicity to fungi when tested in agar. These considerations led to the agar test in petri dishes being largely abandoned, except as a preliminary test when large numbers of new compounds are being examined to see if they have any toxicity to fungi.

The older literature on the subject contains many references to the toxicity of a wide range of chemicals as determined by the agar test, and the following figures are typical of some of the results obtained:

Chemical	Fungus	Inhibiting Concentration per cent wt/vol.
Coal tar creosote	Coniophora cerebella	0·05
	Lentinus lepideus	0·2
Sodium fluoride	C. cerebella	0·2
Copper sulphate	C. cerebella	0·75
	Poria monticola	1·0
Borax	C. cerebella	0·1 – 0·2

Wood Block Method. To-day laboratory assessment of the toxicity of wood preservatives to fungi is generally carried out by means of the 'wood block method'. This test involves the exposure, to actively growing cultures of wood-rotting fungi, of a number of small blocks of wood which have been impregnated with a graded series of concentrations of the product under trial. The flasks or bottles containing the treated test pieces are kept in a warm room, or incubated, for three months. After this time the pieces are removed and examined for signs of decay and of fungal growth. The loss in dry weight substance due to decay is then estimated and calculated as a percentage of the original dry weight.

There is some variation between different laboratories in the way in which the test fungi for these experiments are cultivated. In Europe they are generally grown on a malt agar medium, but in America they are cultivated on thin strips of untreated wood resting on damp soil.

The technique for carrying out the tests has been described in detail in British Standards No. 838, 2nd edition 1961, *Methods of Test for Toxicity of Wood Preservatives to Fungi,* and in the American Society for Testing Materials Method D-56 T. (See Pl. V. 2 a and b.)

Though the results obtained by the two methods may differ somewhat, particularly for oily preservatives which can evaporate more easily from the small one-inch cube blocks used in the American method than from the oblong blocks (5 × 2·5 × 1·5 cm.) generally employed in Europe, the general conclusions derived from either type of wood block test should be broadly comparable.

A good deal more information about what happens to the preservative in the wood is needed before one can use the figures derived from these tests directly to estimate the retentions required to protect timber in service. Nevertheless these so-called toxic limits, or threshold concentrations i.e. the minimum amount of preservative expressed as its weight per unit volume of wood—do form a basis on which to compare the effective toxicity of the compounds.

The following examples illustrate the toxic limits that have been determined for two preservatives:

Preservative	Test Fungus	Toxic Limits Kgs./m.³
Creosote	Coniophora cerebella	4-6
	Lentinus lepideus	about 12
Sodium Fluoride	Coniophora cerebella	0·5-0·7
	Lentinus lepideus	about 0·1

Toxicity Tests against Insects

It is much more difficult accurately to assess the minimum concentrations of a preservative that will be needed to protect a susceptible timber against insects than against fungal attack. There are a number of reasons why this is so:

1. Many of the insects are seasonal in their breeding habits.
2. The different stages of the insect—eggs, larvae and adults —often differ in their susceptibility to poisons.
3. Insects have powers of discrimination and can refuse to lay their eggs on treated surfaces, or to eat treated wood.
4. Many insects will attack wood only when it is in a particularly susceptible condition—for example, the larvae of *Lyctus* beetles can thrive only in sapwood that contains starch; while Death Watch larvae flourish only in wood that is partly decayed.

Insecticidal wood preservatives are often used to treat wood already infested with insects. This means that such fluids must have an immediate killing action as well as a long term preservative effect. Obviously a different type of test will be required to distinguish between, and to assess, these two different types of action.

Insecticides are often classified according to their mode of action, thus:

1. Stomach poisons.
2. Contact poisons.
3. Respiratory poisons.

The type of test chosen must be adapted to the nature of the insecticidal action.

In view of the difficulties involved no standard methods have been adopted in this country, but the British Standards

Institution has the matter under consideration and it may presently be found possible to agree on some standard methods.

In Germany a standard method, DIN 52-621 has been published. In this test young (so-called 'egg') larvae of the House Longhorn beetle are confined on to one face of small blocks of treated wood and the numbers that survive are counted after four and after twelve weeks, and the amount of boring into the wood which has taken place is measured.

Another German standard test is designed to assess the efficacy of insecticidal preparations in killing larvae in the wood. For this test living larvae of the House Longhorn and of the Common Furniture Beetle are inserted into pre-drilled holes in untreated test blocks and are left to bore into the wood for three months at 28°C or for six months at 20°C. Before the blocks are treated with preservative the ends are sealed with paraffin wax. The insecticide is then applied by brushing on one, two or three coats and the amounts absorbed are measured by weighing the blocks before and after treatment. After a further five months storage at 20°C in an atmosphere of 70-75% relative humidity, the treated and the control blocks are split open and the number of living and dead larvae and their distance from the treated surface determined. The efficacy of the preservative is assessed from the percentage of dead larvae in the total number of larvae recovered.

Yet a third type of test used in Germany is designed to determine the toxic limit of wood preservatives—that is to say, the minimum loading of preservative that will prevent attack by larvae of wood-boring insects. In this test larvae of the House Longhorn or of the Furniture Beetle, are inserted into pre-drilled holes made in a series of blocks, which have been impregnated with graded concentrations of the preservative under test. After four, and after twelve weeks—and occasionally six months—storage the blocks are split up and the numbers of dead and living animals are counted. The toxic limit is usually expressed as the interval between the highest concentration at which living insects were found and the lowest that killed all the larvae.

Up to the present facilities for carrying out standard tests of wood preservatives against insects have not been available in

Great Britain, and hence such data are lacking about many insecticidal wood preservatives manufactured in this country. It is to be hoped that this situation will be remedied in the near future.

Few controlled service tests against insects, other than termites, have so far been set up anywhere in the world. The results of treatments designed to eliminate existing infestations are extremely difficult to assess as the degree of infestation is so variable and often much of the infested material is removed before treatment is carried out.

K. M. Harrow reported in the *New Zealand Timber Journal*, June 1960, the results of a practical exposure test of treated timber to Furniture Beetles (*Anobium*). This test was carried out in an experimental building constructed partly of impregnated and partly of untreated timber. Here several thousand beetles were released annually for four consecutive years after its construction. Eleven years later most of the untreated wood was found to be infested but careful searching failed to discover any infestation in the boarding that had been treated with boric acid and sodium fluoride, Tanalith U, or zinc chloride at quite low concentrations. The results of this service test provide good evidence that the retentions, at least of non-volatile preservatives, found to be effective against insects in laboratory tests, can give satisfactory protection in practice to timber that is not exposed to the weather.

Field tests against termites have been laid down in a number of countries and the results of international termite tests have been published. An interesting fact that emerges from these tests is that the different species of termites, (of which there are hundreds) vary greatly in their susceptibility to poisons. Some preservatives proved to be more effective in certain regions than in others, and so the results obtained in one country must be applied with caution to other parts of the world where different species of termites exist. Such results show how desirable it is that findings from field tests should be available from the region in which the preservative is to be used.

Recently standardised laboratory tests, using known numbers of termites, have been devised, notably in Australia as well as in Germany, and it is reported that reliable and consistent results can be obtained.

Tests Against Marine Borers

Practical trials with baulks of impregnated timber placed in the sea were set up many years ago in various parts of the world. The results of these have been published in the *Proceedings of the American Wood Preserving Association*, Vol. 45, 1949, and elsewhere. In such tests the treated piles have generally to be observed over a long period of years before reliable conclusions can be drawn from the results. Efforts are therefore being made to devise laboratory methods for the evaluation of preservatives against Marine Borers. Becker, at the Material Prüfungsamt in Berlin, has had considerable success in breeding *Limnoria* and *Teredo* in aquaria in the laboratory, for use in controlled tests on small treated test pieces.

Penetrability Tests

Liquids differ in the ease with which they can penetrate into wood. The rate at which a liquid moves through a porous material depends on its viscosity, and on its surface tension, as well as on the nature of the material itself. As already explained (see page 10) the permeability of wood varies greatly even within a single species of timber, and is immensely greater along, as compared with across, the grain. In order to assess and compare the penetrating power of different liquids it is therefore absolutely essential to use as test material very carefully selected straight grained samples of wood conditioned to a precise moisture content. Standard methods for assessing the penetrating power of a preservative applied by brushing or by immersion have been proposed in Germany, see DIN 52-618.

The penetration of water-borne preservatives is more complex than that of oils as actual diffusion of salts occurs in addition to movement of liquid through the capillary spaces in the wood. The penetration of salts applied by diffusion methods must, of course, be studied in green timber saturated with moisture. Where the solutions are more or less colourless appropriate reagents must be sprayed on to the freshly cut surface of the test pieces to produce a colour and thus reveal wherever the preservative has penetrated. For example the presence of boric acid can be detected by spraying the surface with a 1·0% acidified solution of polyvinyl alcohol, followed by the application of o·1 N iodine solution. This reacts to produce a deep blue colour wherever boric or borate is present.

Permanence Tests

It is axiomatic that a preservative must remain in the wood if it is to continue to protect it. The concentration of preservative originally introduced into the wood may fall in the course of time as the result of several different causes:

1. Volatilisation—part or all of the material may evaporate away.
2. Leaching—solution and washing out of preservative.
3. Chemical changes in composition, e.g. polymerisation.

In addition a redistribution of the preservative within the treated timber may occur—for instance immediately after brush treatment the surface layers may contain sufficient preservative to protect them, but if the preservative continues to move into the wood and to distribute itself evenly throughout the thickness of a large baulk the concentration in the surface layers may drop below the toxic limit necessary to inhibit fungal and insect attack. Such a redistribution of preservatives is particularly prone to occur in poles, when liquids may slowly flow down under the influence of gravity, while at the same time moisture moving up from the wet soil may carry up salts that are not fully fixed in the wood.

Prospective users of preservatives have always tended to regard with sceptical doubt any attempt to predict practical performance from the results of laboratory tests, as it is very difficult to imitate the weathering influences to which timber in the open is exposed. However if we can devise laboratory tests for permanence which will correctly rate those long established preservatives about which records already exist from field trials and service performance, then we can feel some confidence that the results of such tests on new products will give a reasonably reliable indication as to how they will stand up to the passage of time.

In the revised edition (1961) of the British Standard *Method for Tests of Toxicity of Wood Preservatives to Fungi*, a procedure has been described by which the resistance of a preservative to evaporation and leaching can be assessed. This involves ex-

Standard laboratory methods for assessing toxicity of wood preservatives

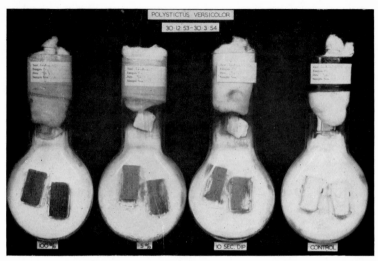

European method in Kolle flasks using nutrient agar on which
to grow test fungi

Soil block method commonly used in U.S.A. *(Crown copyright)*

posing the treated blocks for four days in distilled water which is changed regularly, followed by three days drying at 50°C; the whole process being carried out four times. The resistance to decay of impregnated test blocks after this treatment is compared with that of similar blocks which have not been so treated. The change in the toxic limits observed gives a reliable indication of the susceptibility of the preservative to leaching and evaporation. A more severe leaching test is proposed for preservatives intended for use in exceptionally exposed situations, as for instance in contact with tropical soil, or for marine or cooling tower work. This consists of continuous extraction for 300 hours of the treated samples with a stream of warm distilled water in a Soxhlet apparatus. Any preservative that remains effective after such a severe leaching treatment must obviously be extremely resistant to weathering. Preservatives that have shown up well in this test have, in fact, proved to be effective under similar severe conditions in water cooling towers.

Tests of Corrosive Action

One method of testing the corrosive action of any wood preserving fluid is by suspending strips of clean mild steel and other metals in solutions of the preservative, and then, after cleaning the samples (e.g. electrolytically) weighing the amounts of metal removed.

Another method is to embed nails or screws into treated wood which is then kept in a damp atmosphere, at say 90% relative humidity. The condition of the metal fastenings is examined after prolonged periods of exposure and the amount of rusting and corrosion is noted.

Interpretation of Laboratory Tests

The scepticism mentioned earlier as to the practical value of the findings of laboratory tests was at one time fully justified. Figures indicating a high toxicity to fungi, which had been derived from agar tests in petri dishes did not by themselves prove that a chemical would be a good preservative for timber. It is unfortunately true that results of such tests have, without much justification, been used in the past to promote the sales of new preservatives.

However the situation is now changing. With improved

methods, using wood as the medium on which the preservatives are tested, and with a wide range of wood-rotting test fungi— including species capable of causing soft rot as well as the typical brown and white rots—together with a drastic weathering procedure, truly reliable results can be obtained.

Dr Colley, an international authority on wood preservation, concluded as the result of an exhaustive survey of existing test methods, that 'The soil block technique (for testing preservatives) incorporating a weathering procedure, is a practical, rapid method of bio-assay, and the results obtained from this method are in general agreement with accelerated stake and long term pole diameter post tests on the same or similar preservatives', and 'that the use of the laboratories' controlled weathering procedure will provide a means for determining truly effective threshold retentions for oil type and salt type preservatives for comparable service requirements.'

Because the results of laboratory tests have been misused for advertising purposes it does not follow that such results are in themselves unreliable, if they are considered objectively in their right context. It is the author's considered opinion that it is now possible, from the results of properly planned laboratory tests, to assess with a fair degree of accuracy the practical value of any substance for the preservation of wood.

When a prospective purchaser of a wood preservative is presented with the results of laboratory experiments on the product he should satisfy himself that the tests have been carried out (A) in an independent laboratory, or according to some standard recognised method, (B) with a number of organisms including those to which the timber in question will be exposed (for example, effectiveness against fungi does not necessarily imply effectiveness against insects and vice versa), and (C) so as to indicate whether the preservative is likely to be permanent in the wood—i.e. is neither volatile nor, if the product is to be used in the open, readily washed out.

He should also seek information as to any possible effect that the product may have on the wood itself (e.g. making it hygroscopic) or on metal fastenings with which the treated wood may come in contact. He should also enquire whether the product has any objectionable characteristics, such as smell, which might limit its use in buildings, and whether its use involves any health hazards to operators or to those handling the treated wood.

Finally the purchaser should find out what effect the treatment has on the flammability of the wood, and whether any special fire hazards arise during the application of the preservative.

REFERENCES

Becker, G., and Schulze, B. *Wiss. Abh. Matpr. amt.*, **7**, 76-83, 1950.

British Standard 838, 1961.

Colley, R. M. 'The Evaluation of Wood Preservatives', *Bell System Tech. J.*, **32** (1), 120-69; (2), 425-505, 1953.

Harrow, K. M. 'A Field Test of Preservatives in Building Construction', *N.Z. Timber J.*, June 1960.

Smith, D. N. 'Field Tests on Wood Preservatives used for Pressure Treatment', *For. Prod. Res. Bull.*, **32**, 1954.

CHAPTER VI

IN-SITU TREATMENTS FOR ERADICATION AND PRESERVATION

Nowhere is the old adage 'prevention is better than cure' more true than in the field of wood preservation. It is always much cheaper, and far more effective, to treat timber before it is built into a structure, than to attempt to do so after it is already in position. Nevertheless we are faced with the problem of conserving and maintaining millions of old buildings in many of which pests and decay have already become established, and by careful and thorough treatment of the woodwork in them it is sometimes possible greatly to prolong their lives.

Broadly speaking in-situ treatments are applied mainly in buildings and in boats; and, to a more limited extent, to poles affected by incipient decay at ground level. The question of boats and poles are dealt with in Chapters IX, and X. In this chapter woodwork in buildings will be considered. This suffers damage as a result of either:

1. Fungal decay—e.g. Dry Rot and Wet Rot, or
2. Insect attack e.g. Woodworm, Death Watch Beetle, or House Longhorn Beetle.

FUNGAL DECAY

Fungal decay can occur only where there is persistant dampness. Apart from accidental leakage due to plumbing defects, moisture can reach the woodwork in a building either as the result of rainwater penetrating through leaking roofs, faulty gutters and down pipes—conditions which can be cured; or from dampness rising up walls in which there is no damp proof course—a condition which is very difficult to remedy.

The first thing to do when dealing with decay of woodwork in a building is to seek the source of the dampness, and to do everything possible to dry out the timber, and to prevent further access of moisture. Theoretically this should ensure that there is no further spread of decay, but in practice it is often very difficult—for instance in an old stone building—to ensure

Injecting beams attacked by Death Watch Beetle, with insecticide

Funnel method being used on Westminster Abbey timbers to obtain deep penetration of insecticide

permanently dry conditions. It is therefore wise to treat with pre-servative all existing sound timber exposed during the repair work. It is seldom worth while attempting to treat timber that already shows signs of incipient decay, unless it has some special interest or artistic value. Wood affected by decay is usually much weakened and has to be replaced for reasons of safety.

Eradication of Dry Rot

The eradication of true dry rot presents a special problem. The term 'Dry Rot' is applied to the decay of timber which is brought about by certain specialised fungi, notably *Merulius lacrymans*, the Dry Rot fungus. These possess water-conducting strands which enable them to spread for considerable distances over and through inert materials such as masonry and brick-work. Wood attacked by dry rot usually breaks up into rectangular blocks and crumbles to powder when rubbed between finger and thumb. On the surface of the rotted wood there is often a silvery grey skin of fungal mycelium.

When an outbreak of dry rot has become established it may spread rapidly. When conditions are favourable for the growth of the fungus the whole floor of an average sized room may become so severely decayed within two years as to be thoroughly unsafe. The strands of the fungus are capable of penetrating through masonry and brickwork for many yards, seeking out and attacking any timber such as fixing blocks and bond timbers that are embedded in the walls. Unless steps are taken to sterilise any walls infected with these strands the fungus may grow out from the brickwork, after the decayed wood has been removed, and re-infest new timber used in repairs.

Before carrying out the sterilisation treatment all the decayed wood should be cut away, 18 inches or so beyond last signs of visible decay or fungal growth. Particular care must be taken to seek for and remove any pieces of timber embedded in the walls, such as fixing blocks and bond timbers.

Sterilisation of Walls

In the past it has generally been customary to heat the surface of the brick or stonework with a blow-lamp flame before applying a fungicide. This heating, as usually carried out, is of very little value. Only the surface of the wall is heated sufficiently to kill

G

any infection, and fungus growths in the mortar joints remain unaffected. Also the use of a blow-lamp in a confined space where there is much timber around involves a certain fire risk, and it is therefore wiser not to use one on brickwork in a roof space. Nor should a flame *ever* be applied to decayed timber as this ignites very easily and may continue to smoulder for a long time without being detected.

With the development of modern potent fungicides there is really no need for preliminary heat treatments of infected walls, though they do help to dry out a wall and to increase the penetration of the fungicide and so may sometimes be considered worth while.

Various fungicides including mercuric chloride, copper sulphate, sodium fluoride and magnesium silicofluoride, have been recommended in the past, but these have now largely been superseded by more potent products. The two chemicals most widely used to-day are sodium pentachlorophenate (S.P.C.P.) and sodium orthophenylphenate (S.O.P.P.).* There is very little difference between these two as regards their toxicity to the Dry Rot Fungus, but S.O.P.P. is pleasanter to use as its solution is less irritating to the skin. Both these substances are generally applied at a concentration of 5% (about 8 oz. to the gallon of water), a small amount of wetting agent being added to improve the penetration of the liquid into the wall. Ready mixed solutions of these chemicals are available under various proprietary names, and it is often convenient to use one of these. (See Appendix.) But when very large amounts of the solutions are required it will be found more economical to purchase the chemicals themselves from the manufacturers and to make up the solution on the site.

The solution chosen may be applied by swabbing on freely with a distemper brush, but when a large area has to be covered it is more convenient to apply it by spraying. A coarse spray, without too much pressure, should be used to avoid atomising the solution. All surfaces of the wall to be treated should be sprayed until the solution shows signs of running off. Where dampness is likely to persist, and where the fungus has penetrated deeply into the wall, it may be desirable to attempt complete impregnation of the wall at strategic points, so as to pre-

* Sold as 'Topane W.S.' by Imperial Chemical Industries Ltd.

vent any lateral spread of the fungus within the thickness of the wall. In this way a barrier of fungicide can be created which will prevent the fungus reaching window and door frames, etc., which have so far escaped attack. This method of treatment is most easily carried out where the top of the wall is open—e.g. where a rotten wall plate has been removed—but it can also be successfully applied to a vertical surface by drilling into it a series of $\frac{3}{4}$ in. holes, 6-9 ins. deep, sloping down into the wall. These should be spaced about 18 ins. apart horizontally, and about three feet apart vertically in staggered rows. They should be filled repeatedly through funnels until fluid appears in holes cut at the bottom of the affected area. Pint bottles with the bottoms cut off make convenient cheap funnels.

After such treatment a wall must be left to dry out before redecoration can be undertaken, as an efflorescence of salts on the surface is likely to take place—this, of course, should be brushed off when it appears. In cases where any such efflorescence would be undesirable a fungicidal rendering of zinc oxychloride cement can be applied. This will also prevent any regrowth of fungus on the surface and act as an effective barrier against its spread. This material is somewhat expensive and is probably used to the best advantage as a rendering with which to line openings for window and door frames.

Sterilisation of Timber

Sound timber left in position after the decayed portions have been cut away should be treated, so as to kill any spores left on the surface and to protect it against the possibility of subsequent re-infection.

Various preservatives can be used for this purpose, the choice depending on the nature of the building. If there is any risk of the preservative bleeding through paint, or staining plaster, tar oils should be avoided, and a solvent type or water-borne preservative should be used. If a colourless, non-staining preservative is required a 5% solution of sodium pentachlorophenate, or of a mixture of equal parts of borax and boric acid may be used. Where the absence of smell is important, as in a food store or shop, water-borne preservatives are the most suitable type, but for timber in the open and in very damp situations where there may be a risk of leaching solvent type preservatives are best.

The preservative should be applied freely by brush or spray, giving at least two flowing coats, the second being applied after the first has soaked into the wood. Particular care should be taken to work the preservative well into joints and cracks where fungus spores may have lodged.

Normally every piece of timber that shows any indications of being infected should be cut out, but under special circumstances rigid adherence to this counsel of perfection may lead to great and unnecessary expense. For example the end of a main beam may be found to be slightly decayed to a depth of half an inch or so on its surface, but may still retain more than sufficient strength to carry the load that it is bearing. To cut off the end might involve shoring up the beam and the splicing on of a new end with supporting metal plates—an operation that would probably cost hundreds of pounds. In such a case in-situ treatment to arrest any further spread of the rot is justified, particularly if the source of dampness can be removed and dry conditions maintained in the future.

The sides of the beam should be fully exposed and any softened wood cut away from the surface. The underlying sound wood should then be freely and repeatedly swabbed with a preservative that penetrates freely. In addition a series of half-inch holes should be bored in staggered rows in the upper surface of the beam to two-thirds of its depth. These should be filled repeatedly through a funnel with a liquid preservative so as to form within the beam a barrier of preservative that will prevent any further spread of the rot, even if damp should persist or recur.

An alternative to this method is to inset into the holes a paste made with water soluble salts, such as a borax-boric mixture, which will slowly diffuse across the whole thickness of the beam.

After treatment the end of the beam should be left exposed at the sides so that air can circulate freely around it.

In-situ treatment may also be necessary to conserve ancient woodwork of historical interest or artistic value. Carved and ornamental woodwork, such as panelling, can often be taken down from a wall so that it can be effectively treated with a preservative on all faces. If such panelling is in a damp condition when it is removed it must be dried out slowly, so that it does not shrink or crack unduly, before the wood preservative is applied. If new timber is used to strengthen the old it should be well seasoned and thoroughly treated with a preservative.

When the decay has been caused by a fungus less virulent than *Merulius lacrymans* (the Dry Rot Fungus)—e.g. when it is of the 'Wet Rot' type caused by *Coniophora cerebella*—sterilisation of the walls may safely be omitted, but it is always a wise precaution to treat with preservative all the sound timber used during repairs.

Treatment of Timber Used in Repairs

Preservative treatment should always be given to all new timber used to replace that which has been cut away during repairs. Joinery can be adequately treated on the site by thorough brushing (three successive coats), or by immersion in a bath of the preservative. For new structural timbers, such as joists, wood that has been treated by an impregnation process should be used wherever possible. The use of impregnated timber is particularly desirable when it is likely that dampness will persist in spite of all that can be done to alleviate it, by improved ventilation etc. Unfortunately such timber is not always available, especially in the more remote parts of the country. When it cannot be obtained some form of tank or trough should be contrived in which the structural timbers can be steeped. Old stone buildings in the wetter parts of the British Isles, cottages with wattle and daub walls, and houses on heavy clay soils with solid brick walls lacking an effective damp proof course, are a few examples of the kinds of buildings in which impregnated timber can be used with particular advantage.

INSECT ATTACK

It is not possible within the scope of this book to deal fully with all the problems involved in the successful eradication of timber insects from buildings. Such problems depend in the first instance on the species of insect, the kind of timber involved, and the degree of infestation, and secondly on the nature and construction of the building. The need for a careful survey and for accurate indentification of the pests must be emphasised, otherwise much money and effort may be wasted without any useful result being achieved.

The nature of the damage, and the identity of the insects that have been responsible, can be determined by reference to the author's earlier book *Dry Rot and other Timber Troubles* or to the literature published by the Forest Products Research Laboratory and the British Wood Preserving Association. If any doubt remains, samples of affected wood and specimens of the insects should be submitted to an independent authority, such as the Timber Development Association.

An infestation often dies out naturally and in that case, though evidence of old damage will be found, there will be no traces of activity. In most old houses there is a certain amount of woodworm damage along the sapwood edges of the floor boards, but more often than not no living insects can be found, and it may be concluded that the attack died out years ago.

It is critically important to discover whether or not an active infestation exists, and the most careful search should be made for signs of activity such as piles of bore dust and fresh clean exit holes. Beetles will normally be found only during the summer months, but living larvae may be found at any season by cutting into the wood—though prolonged search may be necessary to find them if the wood is only lightly infested.

Since the end of the second World War an active pest control industry has grown up in the United Kingdom. Several firms offer a nation-wide pest eradication service, and it is becoming increasingly usual for house owners to employ such firms to deal with infestations of woodworm. Their skilled operatives working under the supervision of competent surveyors are likely to be much more efficient than a builder's labourer applying a solution with a paint brush. The house owner may rely on the workmanship of any firm that is a member of the British Wood Preserving Association which has laid down a code of practice which all its members have agreed to observe.

Some of these servicing companies are prepared to issue a guarantee that they will retreat, free of cost, should there be within twenty years, any recurrence of the pests—in the areas that have been treated. Obviously no one can guarantee that the pests will not appear in parts of the house that have not received treatment. Even if every insect in the house were killed fresh ones might be introduced in old furntiture, or the beetles may fly in through the window.

Other firms, who carry out equally good work, maintain that the permanence of the superficially applied preservatives now in general use cannot be foretold precisely, and that it is unrealistic to demand, or to give, such long term guarantees.

These specialist services are, of course, expensive, and not every small infestation warrants their employment. If only one or two rafters, or a few floor boards, are found to be infected the house owner, or his builder, should treat those particular timbers with several flowing coats of a preservative and then keep them under observation, inspecting the timbers annually for any signs of fresh activity.

Eradication of Woodworm

For those who wish to practise 'Do it yourself' eradication the following procedure should be followed:

1. *Inspection.* Equip yourself with a powerful electric torch, or an adequate length of lead to a shielded electric light bulb. Examine methodically and carefully all the suspected timbers, especially any in the roof space, paying particular attention to the edges of boards and arrises of the beams, where sapwood, if any, will be found. Look out for any signs of activity—e.g. piles of bore dust and new clean exit holes. Prod into any wood in which exit holes are found to discover the depth and extent of the damage.

Infestation is most likely to occur where there has been incipient decay and persistent dampness. The older types of plywood—e.g. Birch plywood bonded with animal glues—are particularly susceptible to attack. The heartwood of Baltic Redwood (Scots Pine), and Oak, are by nature highly resistant to infestation and are only attacked when they have been softened by decay.

Collect any beetles or larvae found and examine them under a lens or microscope. In at least nine cases out of ten it will be found that the insect responsible for the damage is the Common Furniture Beetle, but if there is any doubt a sample should be submitted to an authority as indicated above.

In the older buildings, where the timbers are of generous dimensions and consist mainly of heartwood, woodworm damage is seldom sufficiently severe to affect the structural stability of a floor or roof, but individual joists or rafters, particularly those with waney edges, consisting mainly or entirely of sapwood, may have to be replaced. Floor boards also are frequently found to be so severely tunnelled along the edges as to require replacement.

2. *Treatment.* Before applying an insecticide to the timbers which it has been decided to retain, their surfaces should be freed from dust, and any softened, powdery wood along the end of the rafters should be cut away with a draw knife. Any old furniture, packing cases, wicker baskets and odd scraps of wood should be removed from a roof space, attic or cellar in which woodworm has been found.

After the wood has been cleaned down and the rubbish removed a really thorough dressing with insecticide (see page 91) should be given; either brushing on the solution very freely, or spraying it on, until the wood appears wet, with a low pressure nozzle designed to give a coarse spray. It is important that the fluid should penetrate into all the cracks and joints, as these are the places where the beetles prefer to lay their eggs.

While it is not possible by this surface treatment to ensure that every insect in the wood has been killed, it will protect the surface against the risk of re-infestation. After a few years any surviving insects must emerge and if they cannot re-infest the wood, the attack will cease.

After treating flooring or panelling the holes in the surface should be filled with wax (insecticidal waxes which give added protection are available) so that any fresh holes formed subsequently to the treatment may be detected.

Death Watch Beetle

As already explained (see page 24) the Death Watch Beetle is mainly a pest of large-sized oak timbers. It seldom, if ever, attacks completely sound wood, but generally becomes established in the decayed ends of beams which have been exposed to persistent dampness. So the first consideration in dealing with an infestation is to find out the source of the dampness. Much can be done to arrest the progress of the attack by eliminating the damp and by improving the circulation of air around the ends of beams and below floors.

As Death Watch Beetle works its way deep into the core of large beams it is difficult to reach it by any surface application of insecticides. An attempt is often made, therefore, to impregnate the timber by injecting the solution through holes bored in the upper surface of the beam down to $\frac{1}{2}$ to $\frac{2}{3}$ of its depth. (See Pl. VI, 1.) It is wiser not to force fluid into such holes under very high pressure as it may then be merely forced out through splits in the wood. It is more laborious, but possibly more effective, to stand large funnels in these holes and to fill them repeatedly with insecticide, which will then slowly flow down into the wood under the influence of gravity, and diffuse itself throughout the tunnels and workings of the larvae in the centre of the beam. (See Pl. VI, 2.)

House Longhorn Beetle

If attack by *Hylotropes bajulus* is suspected (this is common only in parts of Surrey) the local authority should be informed, as the eradication of this insect is the subject of certain by-laws. If the identity of the suspected infestation is confirmed, expert advice should be sought and steps taken to eradicate it without delay.

Choice of Insecticides

For treating woodwork in barns, stables and outhouses, where woodworm attack is often severe on account of the relatively high moisture content of the timber, good brushing quality creosote (conforming to B.S. 3051) is quite suitable and much the cheapest product available. But in a house or church where a strong odour of tar oils may be undesirable, and where it is important not to cause staining in adjacent plaster or stonework, it is generally preferable to use a solvent type preservative consisting of insecticidal chemicals dissolved in kerosene or white spirit, or a water-borne preservative containing an insecticide.

Modern insecticides properly formulated are so much more effective than home-made remedies that it pays to use one of the well-known proprietary products. (See Appendix.) Most of these contain a mixture of chemicals, some of which are primarily intended to kill the larvae in the wood, while others of a more persistent nature are designed to protect the wood against subsequent re-infestation. Many of the modern formulations contain a proportion of dieldrin together with monochloronaphthalene and metallic naphthenates. The makers' instructions should be carefully followed and any precautions regarding the protection of operatives and prevention of fire should be rigorously observed.

For some time after the timber has been sprayed with a flammable preparation based on white spirit or kerosene, the surface remains capable of propagating a self supporting flame initiated from a small source. After applying an oily preservative good ventilation should be provided in any roof space so as to allow the oil to dissipate, and during this drying period extra precautions against fire should be observed, and no naked lights should be permitted. This increased fire risk is likely to persist for two to seven days depending on the nature of the solvent used. If an aqueous solution is used care must be taken to prevent its wetting electrical switches or poorly insulated electrical wiring.

Cost of In-Situ Treatment

In-Situ treatments are inevitably expensive for a number of reasons:

1. The timbers must be cleaned before solutions can be applied. In roof treatments this often involves removing deep deposits of dirt by means of an industrial vacuum cleaner.
2. Hidden timbers may have to be exposed involving much work in the taking up of floor boards and removing of panelling from the walls.
3. Extensive redecoration of walls and ceilings may become necessary.
4. The cost of the labour is high as skilled workmen must be employed, often at a considerable distance from their homes.
5. The solutions used are often more expensive than those used in pre-treatment.

Owners of property are often in the dark as to what the cost of an eradication treatment should be, and they would therefore be well advised to obtain estimates from several different firms before placing an order for work to be carried out.

If an active attack of *Dry Rot* is found it must be dealt with drastically and immediately—otherwise the owner will almost certainly be involved in greater expense at a later date

If the decay is found to be of the *Wet Rot* type, and is localised to the area which is damp, the work involved is usually builders' work and there is no need to go to the expense of calling in pest eradication experts. The source of dampness should be sought and everything possible done to dry out the timber and to keep it dry. And of course it is only common sense to repair at once any timbers of which the structural stability has been impaired.

If it is a question of *Woodworm* the decision whether or not to go to the expense of a full scale eradication should be decided primarily on the degree of the activity observed—though some may feel it worth while in any case for the sake of the peace of mind thus obtained.

CHAPTER VII

PRESERVATION OF BUILDING TIMBER

IT has often been argued that, as dry rot does not develop in houses that are properly built and adequately maintained, it is needless expense to protect timber against its occurrence. While this statement is correct as far as it goes, it ignores two very important facts—(a) that by no means all houses are properly looked after by owners and tenants, and (b) that there are other hazards to be guarded against more common than the true Dry Rot caused by *Merulius lacrymans*. Also there are certain new factors that have altered the whole picture during the last fifty years. One of these is the increasing proportion of susceptible sapwood now being used in building timber. Another is the reduction in dimensions of structural timbers to the minimum consistent with safety provided that the whole cross section is sound. In the better built Victorian houses the wood used was generally Baltic Redwood, the heartwood of which is resistant to fungal decay and practically immune to attack by woodworm. As scarcely any sapwood was included we often find the woodwork in these houses still in excellent condition to-day; whereas thousands of houses built during the interwar years are already seriously infested with woodworm and much external joinery has decayed owing to wet rot.

It is difficult to get any sort of figures for the average cost of repairing decayed window and door frames, but this kind of work, which involves skilled patching and splicing by craftsmen, is invariably very expensive in proportion to the actual volume of wood that has to be replaced. To quote an actual example that recently came to the author's notice: In a well maintained single story building, architect designed, and erected in 1951 by a reputable builder, extensive decay of window and door frames had already occurred in 1959, necessitating repairs and patching which cost over £70. It would probably be true to say that it costs as many pounds to effect such repairs as it would have cost shillings to protect the timber with preservative in the first instance, particularly as extensive redecoration is often necessary after such repairs have been carried out.

If an extensive infestation by the Common Furniture Beetle becomes established in the structural timber and joinery the cost of eradication can easily amount to several hundreds of pounds. As has already been intimated, such infestation in nineteenth-century houses rarely leads to any failure of structural timbers as these were of generous proportions and contained very little sapwood. However the situation in the future is likely to be very different, and replacement, not merely surface treatment, of infested roof timbers may often be necessary once woodworm has become established.

Many servicing companies are now having to deal with outbreaks of dry rot and woodworm that should never have been allowed to become established. Though many older houses will doubtless require their services for a long time to come, one can look forward to the time when more effort will be put into preventing these attacks than into eradicating them. Already the timber trade is waking up to the need for supplying ready treated timber on demand, and there is no doubt that the time will come when most architects will insist on pre-treatment of building timbers. At present they often hesitate to do so on account of the difficulties and delays in obtaining supplies of properly treated dry timber.

The two major hazards against which building timbers will need protection in the future would appear to be:

(*a*) Insect attack, mainly by Furniture Beetles.
(*b*) Wet Rot in exposed joinery.

The means by which effective protection can be given at low cost are discussed below.

Use of Naturally Durable Timbers

In this country it is now comparatively rare for highly durable timbers to be used for carcassing or interior joinery. Occasionally rafters or joists in old buildings are replaced with Oak so as to match the existing timber, but only if these timbers are completely free of sapwood should their preservative treatment be omitted. If Western Red Cedar is used for joinery no treatment is necessary, and it is doubtful if it is worth while treating Canadian grown Douglas Fir as this usually contains only a small proportion of sapwood and the heartwood will not readily absorb liquids. The other softwoods commonly used for building purposes in this country, such as Baltic Redwood (Scots Pine), Whitewood (Spruce) and Hemlock, are all more or less susceptible to fungal and insect attack and should receive treatment.

The naturally durable hardwoods often used for block and strip flooring do not require treatment if there is no sapwood present, but Oak flooring containing a proportion of sapwood should be treated as it may already be infested with eggs or larvae of *Lyctus* beetles. In France Oak flooring that contains sapwood is often treated with boron solutions to make it as resistant to insect attack as the heartwood. If naturally durable timbers, such as Oak and Gurjun, are used for window sills, wood of selected quality should be chosen, free from knots, crossgrain and sapwood, and any pieces showing the slightest sign of incipient decay (dote) should be rejected.

Choice of Treatment

When deciding what treatment to specify for building timber it must be borne in mind that it is necessary to protect the timber on a long term basis against pests that may not arrive on the scene until many years after the house has been built. It is therefore essential that any preservative used should remain unchanged in the wood for a very long time without losing its effectiveness. It is equally important that the depth of penetration should be greater than that of any splits or cracks that may appear when the timber eventually dries down to its equilibrium content with the atmosphere of the building.

The persistence of some treatments is already well known from records of their performance under practical conditions. These include impregnation with water-borne preservatives containing alkali chromates, and treatment with boron compounds by the diffusion process. Leaching out of water soluble preservatives from timber inside a house is never likely to be sufficient seriously to reduce the effective concentration of preservative, except quite locally. For instance, if there were a persistent leak below a gutter the worst that would probably happen would be a small localised area of wet rot, because no rot could possibly spread into the surrounding unleached areas.

This opinion is supported by the records of the long lasting protection given to pit props in damp coal mines by such easily leached water soluble salts as sodium fluoride. Conditions in these mines were far more humid than would ever be tolerated in a dwelling house. In buildings, particularly in roofs where quite high temperatures can occur, loss of preservative is more likely to take place through volatilisation than as a result of leaching.

The first question that the builder or architect has to decide is whether to have the timber pre-treated by a wood preserving company or to have it treated on the site by building operatives. In some parts of the country which are remote from treating plants there may be no alternative to the latter course as the cost of transporting timber from the plant to the site may well be prohibitive, and, unfortunately, up to the present few timber merchants carry stocks of treated timber.

The advantages of using pre-treated timber from a reputable treating company are, firstly that the buyer has the assurance that the timber has been adequately treated and contains a specified amount of preservative, and secondly that the treated timber is in a condition fit for immediate use. The disadvantage is that some cutting of the treated timber on the site may expose untreated wood in the core of the pieces which may not subsequently receive the secondary brush application necessary to protect it.

If building timber is to be impregnated under pressure with a water-borne preservative the following retentions of dry salts may be specified for structural timbers for internal use:

Copper-chrome preservatives, 0·4 lbs./cub. ft.
Fluoride-arsenate-chromate-dinitrophenol, 0·25 lbs./cub. ft.
Boron preservatives, 0·35 lbs./cub. ft. (boric acid equivalent).

If the timber is to be treated on the site arrangements should be made to provide a tank in which the pieces can be steeped for at least ten minutes. If the quantity to be treated does not warrant setting up a treating tank all the pieces of wood, after having been cut to their final shapes, should be given three full flowing brushed-on coats of preservative. However toxic and effective a preservative may be, one brush application of it cannot be expected to confer long lasting protection.

Choice of Preservative Chemical

In these days architects and builders are confronted with a bewildering choice of preservatives, each backed up with impressive sales literature describing, in more or less technical terms, the particular advantages of the product in question. The preservatives vary greatly in price from say 2/6 a gallon for creosote, to proprietary products at 40/- a gallon. How is one to choose? Are the expensive products all that better than the cheaper ones? Will three applications of a preservative at 10/- a gallon be better than one application of a preservative costing 40/- a gallon? etc. etc.

In the absence of any official approval scheme for wood preservatives, such as already exists for horticultural and agricultural pest control products, any prospective purchaser of a large quantity, who is uncertain on all these points, would be well advised to seek guidance from some official, or completely independent body such as the Forest Products Research Laboratory, or the British Wood Preserving Association.

A purchaser of a proprietary product is entitled to ask what is the nature and concentration of the active ingredient, and this information may enable him to form a basis by which he may compare the prices quoted. To take a simple example, preservatives consisting primarily of sodium pentachlorophenate dissolved in water should not differ very widely in price, provided that the concentration of the active principle is approximately the same in each solution.

Where British Standards specifications for preservatives exist, as for example for creosote and for certain water-borne preservatives, these should always be quoted in orders or contracts, and reference made to the net retentions recommended therein for the particular situations in which the wool will be used.

The following table may be helpful but it must be realised that the risks and hazards of decay in building timbers vary from place to place and from building to building, depending on the purposes for which the timber is used and the care with which it is maintained. It must therefore be emphasised that these recommendations can only be general ones, and that in unusually damp situations a higher degree of protection may be called for.

Class I
Timbers for which protection is essential

Treatment

Timbers in contact with soil or embedded in concrete, e.g. fixing fillets in solid floors; wall plates; roof timbers in laundries, dye houses, waving sheds and other humified buildings; wooden gutters.

Impregnation under pressure with tar oil preservative by empty cell process, or with highly fixed water-borne preservatives of copper-chrome, or copper-chrome-arsenic types.

Class II
Timbers for which protection is desirable

A. Joists, rafters, tiling battens, carcassing timbers containing an appreciable proportion of sapwood.

Impregnation with water-borne preservatives by cylinder, open tank or diffusion process; or steeping for ten minutes in solvent type preservative containing non-volatile antiseptics.

B. External joinery, window and door frames, casement windows, weather boarding.

Steeping for ten minutes; or two full flowing brush coats of solvent type preservative preferably containing a water repellent.

C. Flooring Boards, skirting and picture rails made of softwood.

Brush treatment, at least on under sides or back, with water-borne or solvent type preservative (or light tar oil preservative for flooring only).

Class III
Timbers for which protection is not necessary

Strip and block flooring of durable hardwood free from sapwood, ornamental panelling, internal doors.

Cost of Preservative Treatment

The additional cost of really effective pre-treatment of all the timber used in the construction of an average sized house may amount to approximately 12 to 15% of the cost of the timber. The price of timber increased very much more between 1939 and 1960 than did the cost of preservative treatment, so the economic advantages of preservation have correspondingly increased during that time. Professor Kollmann in a recent article estimated that in Germany adequate preservative treatment of the roofing timbers, joists, and flooring in a house would increase its cost by only 0·9%. This means that that for a house costing £2000 to build effective protection of the woodwork could be provided for £18. This figure is similar to estimates made in this country. Looked upon as a 'once for all' insurance policy against the possibility of fungal decay and

H

insect damage this does not seem a high premium to pay. Even if expensive eradication of woodworm never becomes necessary some decay of joinery and exposed woodwork is only too likely to occur long before a house has become obsolete or reached the end of its useful life.

Industrial Buildings

Less timber is used to-day than formerly in the construction of large industrial buildings, but with the advent of glued and laminated construction there is likely to be renewed interest in the use of timber which has many advantages for roof construction. Wide span supporting roof beams can be made in this way so that storage buildings can be built without internal supporting walls or pillars. Hangars with 150 ft. clear span have recently been built with timber framed roofs. Interesting and graceful shell roofs of flowing design appropriate for public buildings such as churches etc. can be built in this way at reasonable cost. Glu-lam construction is ideally suited for farm buildings such as barns, and recently, in Scotland, a cattle court was built with laminated beams having a span of 78 ft.

Ideally all such timber should receive preservative treatment, but the risk of deterioration due to insect or fungal decay will vary greatly according to the species of wood and the use to which the building is put. Much of the laminated construction is made with Canadian Douglas Fir which is fairly resistant to decay and woodworm attack, and so only if it was to be used in very humid buildings would impregnation of this timber be necessary. But if Baltic Redwood with a fair proportion of sapwood is used it should be impregnated before lamination.

Condensation on roofs in cold weather can easily raise the moisture content of the timbers above the danger level. Many instances of severe decay have occurred in the roofs of buildings in which industrial processes were carried on that involved the humidification of the air. Therefore thorough preservative treatment, preferably by pressure impregnation, should be given to all the roof timbers in such buildings as the following: laundries; dye houses; swimming pools; jam factories; breweries; tanneries; weaving sheds; cattle sheds; etc.

Water-borne preservatives are generally most suitable for this purpose as they are odourless and the treated wood can be painted if so desired. Retentions of dry salts of 0·33 lbs./cub. ft. of Tanalith and of 0·5 lbs./cub. ft. of Celcure would be appropriate for such situations.

In the past there has been a great deal of trouble with decay in the wooden linings of refrigerated ships and cold stores. Moisture finding its way into the interior of the chamber, or through the external walls, condensed on the cold surfaces and seeped into the less cold parts of the framework where the temperature is sufficiently high for decay to proceed, albeit at a fairly slow rate. Decay tends to be more prevalent in the linings of fruit stores kept at 40°-45°F than in meat and fish stores kept at or below freezing point.

One of the first scientific investigations on the prevention of dry rot that was carried out in this country was a search for suitable preservatives that could safely be used on timber in cold stores. It is now thought that the most suitable treatment for such timbers is impregnation with a copper-chrome preservative to give a retention of about 0·5 lb/cub. ft., or with borax-boric mixture. Both of these are odourless and cannot taint the food stuffs in the store. A moisture proof barrier should be incorporated in the walls of any refrigerated chamber, on the warmer side of the insulation, to prevent, so far as possible, the access of moisture to the woodwork and the insulating material.

Surface Finishes

It has been pointed out (see page 31) that wood may be protected against destructive influences by covering its surface with an impervious layer of an inert material. In fact most external joinery has in the past been protected in this way by coating the exposed surfaces with a layer of paint or varnish. Provided that the wood is sound and dry when it is painted, and the paint film is regularly maintained, it will remain sound almost indefinitely. If on the other hand an oil paint is applied to damp or infected wood it may actually increase the risk of decay by retarding the drying out of the wood, particularly if fungal infection can gain access to the back of the wood as, for instance, through unpainted surfaces in contact with brick or plaster work. A great deal of the decay which occurs in window and door frames could be prevented by giving these hidden surfaces of the joinery a good coat of paint. The ordinary pink

priming coat gives very little protection, but proprietary fungicidal primings and protective joinery linings are available. (See
Appendix.)

Surface weathering (see page 29) of exposed wood surfaces
can be prevented by a coating of paint or varnish. During the
last few years there has been an extended use of decorative
hardwoods as an external architectural feature, and of exterior
plywood for cladding, and many attempts have been made to
find a clear finish that will retain the colour and pleasing
appearance of the natural wood. A wide range of proprietary
products has been tested by the Timber Development Association. Out of 55 clear finishes tested not one lasted for more than
two years, even when three coats had been given originally.
Unless considerable improvement can be achieved in the durability of these clear finishes one must accept the fact that
regular retreatment every two years will be necessary to maintain the appearance of fully exposed wood. No particular type
of finish was found to be significantly more durable than any
other, though a linseed oil preparation treated with cyclopenta-
diene appears to possess more than average durability.

The performance of flooring finishes has also been studied by
the Timber Development Association. If wooden flooring is left
untreated it soon becomes dirty in use, and it is very difficult
to keep it clean. Abrasion and wear of the surface will also be
more rapid if the surface is left unprotected than if it is waxed
or polished.

Floor finishes may be classified into three main types:

1. Penetrating oils, such as linseed or mineral oil. These bind
   together the surface fibres of the wood and prevent splintering but do not seal the surface so as to prevent it
   accumulating dirt.

2. Wax finishes. These give a good appearance but have to
   be renewed quite frequently and often become slippery.

3. Floor seals. These materials penetrate the wood to a
   greater or less extent and help to prevent splintering and
   wear. They also provide a thin, transparent, and not too
   slippery, film over the surface which greatly improves the
   appearance and reduces the work of maintainance.

Many new products based on various plastics have been marketed during the last few years, and comparative tests on a large number of these are being carried out by the Timber Development Association. The most widely used products are those based on the phenolic drying oil sealers, but those containing urea formaldehyde resins also give a very hard wearing surface cover to a floor.

CHAPTER VIII

PRESERVATION OF WOODWORK
IN GARDEN AND FARM

DECAY of horticultural woodwork is often unusually rapid, for the simple reason that those very conditions which enable the green plants to flourish are just those most favourable for the growth of wood-rotting fungi. But before applying any preservative treatment to woodwork that will come in contact with plants care must be taken to choose only such chemicals as will not harm the growing crops. The preservation of timber in buildings and in the open present different problems, and it is, of course, in the former that serious damage to plants from noxious fumes is most likely to occur.

Greenhouses and Garden Frames

While it is true to say that a greenhouse built of Baltic Redwood, free of sapwood, and well maintained by regular applications of white lead paint, will last very many years, there are two new factors to-day which have to be taken into consideration. Firstly, most of the Baltic Redwood now being used contains a fairly high proportion of perishable sapwood; and secondly, the high cost of labour and of lead paint discourages owners from repainting their houses as often as they should. Once regular painting is omitted, and if leakage of rainwater is allowed to continue unchecked, rot soon gains entry through unprotected joints and exposed end grain of the wood, and it does not take long for a neglected greenhouse to become derelict and hopelessly decayed. If the manufacturers of wooden greenhouses neglect for much longer to give really effective preservative treatment to the timber it is certain that the demand for them will steadily decrease. Already the light metal framed and concrete glasshouses are becoming increasingly popular as they require little, or no, upkeep.

Durable Timbers Suitable for Greenhouses

The use of naturally durable timbers which do not require

chemical treatment is obviously desirable if they can be relied on to give the same length of service as a treated wood.

Teak is an ideal wood for the construction of glasshouses as it is resistant to decay, moves very little with changes in moisture content, and is reasonably easy to work. It is, however, far too expensive for anything except the highest class of work, such as orchid houses.

Another durable timber which has found particular favour with the makers of greenhouses is Western Red Cedar, as it combines natural durability with lightness, ease of working, and straightness of grain. This last is an important property when long, thin glazing bars of small cross section must remain straight under widely differing conditions of humidity and temperature.

Greenhouses and frames made of Western Red Cedar and left unpainted last fairly well, and it is unquestionably an excellent timber for the purpose, but by extra protection its expectation of life could be extended from 20 years to a probable 50. Experience with untreated Cedar shingles used for roofing suggests that after 15-18 years the natural preservatives are leached out to such a degree that the wood becomes susceptible to decay, and replacement becomes necessary. It is therefore becoming a practice in the U.S.A. to dip Cedar shingles in a preservative before they are fixed in a roof. For the same reason consideration should be given to the treatment of Western Red Cedar greenhouses so as, either to delay the washing out of the natural preservatives, or to enhance the durability of the wood. Regular application every 2-3 years of a coat of linseed oil should help to prevent weathering of the wood and loss of the natural preservatives.

Other durable timbers which have been used to a limited extent for this work include Oak, Guarea, and Idigbo. If Oak is used care must be taken to exclude sapwood and to select timber that is straight grained and free from knots and shakes.

An occasional application, say every three years, of a solvent type preservative to a structure made of one of these fairly durable woods would greatly extend its life. This form of treatment is much quicker and easier to apply than white lead paint, and the solutions themselves are much cheaper. The effect of such treatment would be to check the spread of any small areas of decay that might have become established, either in the joints or in some odd piece of wood of less than average durability.

Given this modicum of protection greenhouses built of durable timbers should last almost indefinitely.

Treatment for Greenhouses and Frames made of Non-Durable Timber

As the majority of the smaller greenhouses are prefabricated in factories it should be relatively easy to arrange for the timbers to be impregnated after they have been fashioned to their final sizes. This would minimise any need for trimming the pieces after treatment.

If there is a treating plant within easy reach of the factory impregnation by vacuum and pressure in a cylinder is the best method to use, as it is easier to control the amount of preservative absorbed, and to achieve deeper and more uniform penetration than is possible by a simple steeping process. The preservatives most generally used are solutions of copper-chrome or copper-chrome-arsenic, and a minimum net retention of 0·5 lbs. of salts per cubic foot of wood should be specified. As conditions in greenhouses are invariably favourable for fungal decay lower retentions than this should never be accepted. The timber, after impregnation with a water-borne preservative, should always be re-dried down to about 18·0% so as to minimise the possibility of shrinkage after assembly.

When it is not possible, or not practicable, to use pressure impregnation the wooden members should be steeped for not less than ten minutes in a tank of solvent type preservative containing copper naphthenate. This should be done after the pieces have been cut to their final sizes, and any necessary holes have been bored in them. The treating solution should contain not less than 2·0% by weight of copper (as metal), which is roughly equivalent to about 25% copper naphthenate. This preservative has been used extensively for horticultural purposes with good results, and for surface application is probably the most suitable of those generally available. It is likely to be more permanent in the wood than solutions of pentachlorophenol in light solvents, especially in timber exposed to high temperatures and sunshine. Copper naphthenate must be used in adequate amounts to afford effective protection as its inherent toxicity to the species of *Poria* that occur in greenhouses is not very high.

The detailed workmanship and finish given to the woodwork will, of course, influence the life of a greenhouse. The better the joints are made, and the fewer the opportunities for water to lodge and to penetrate into the wood, the less will be the risk of premature decay.

For any plane surfaces, or solid doors, plywood impregnated during manufacture with a highly fixed water-borne preservative offers many advantages; but, probably on account of its cost, such plywood has not yet been used to any great extent in greenhouse construction.

Repair of Old Greenhouses

Rot, once established, can spread with surprising rapidity in a greenhouse on account of the high average temperatures maintained in them. For instance at 70°F fungi can grow, and rot can spread, at about twice the speed they could at 50°F. Any timber found to be decayed should be cut out as soon as possible, beyond the last signs of attack, and replaced with timber that has been steeped for at least ten minutes in a copper naphthenate solution. If, however, immediate repairs cannot be undertaken because of plants growing in the house which cannot be disturbed, or if the house is in such a condition that it will shortly have to be replaced and so is not worth spending much money on, the progress of the decay can be checked by either of the following methods: 1. Insert deeply into the partially decayed wood (particularly near the edge of the decayed zone) pellets or cartridges of a highly soluble salt, such as boric-borax mixture, or Cobra salts. 2. Drill $\frac{3}{4}$-$\frac{1}{2}$ inch holes and fill these repeatedly with a strong solution of preservative, using a funnel for the purpose. It is seldom possible to stop rot altogether by these means, but its spread can be slowed down and life of the house usefully extended. At the same time everything should be done to prevent the entry of rain water and to stop any leakage from gutters and down pipes.

Seed Boxes and Mushroom Bed Boards

Seed boxes, which are generally made of fairly thin boards with a high proportion of sapwood, decay rapidly under the warm conditions in a greenhouse or frame. As the wood is in direct contact with a fertile soil which is always kept at the optimum moisture suitable for plant—and fungal—growth, the boxes very often only last for one season. Western Red Cedar boxes may last several years, but some samples of the lower grade Cedar are not highly durable and have been known to decay after only one season's use. So it would seem wise to give even these boxes some sort of antiseptic treatment.

As the roots of the young plants growing in the boxes are likely to come into direct contact with the wood, it is vitally important that any treatment given should have no harmful effect on their growth. For this reason tar oil products, and water soluble salts that are not fully fixed in the wood, should not be used. Solutions of copper naphthenate in light solvent oils have been used with great success over a number of years, but their price, in relation to that of the seed boxes, is rather high, even bought in bulk, and efforts have been made to find something cheaper which will give adequate protection. One way of reducing the cost of solvent type products is to market emulsions of them made up with water which saves the cost of some of the solvent. A concentrated solution of a water-borne preservative that becomes fixed in the wood is now available for horticultural use.

To prolong the life of seed and bulb boxes it is most important that they should be emptied of soil as soon as the plants have been taken out of them. They should then be stacked in narrow tall piles under a roof, so that they can dry out quickly. After the boxes have been cleaned out they should be dipped in an antiseptic which will kill any pathogenic fungi derived from the soil or plant debris, and at the same time increase the resistance of the wood to decay. Probably the cheapest material for this purpose is a 2% solution of copper sulphate, but a really cheap and effective preservative for seed boxes is still needed. It is hoped that shortly some practical trials will be undertaken with selected formulations.

Support Posts for Trees

Cases have been reported where newly planted trees and shrubs have been damaged through being tied to freshly creosoted posts. This damage appears to have occurred more frequently on acid sandy soils, than on calcareous soils in which the tar acids would be more rapidly neutralised. The risk of such damage can be almost entirely eliminated if the creosoted stakes are allowed to weather in the open for three months after they have been treated and before they are used. During this period the more volatile toxic constituents of the creosote will evaporate from the surface layers of the wood. If, for any reason, freshly creosoted posts have to be used care should be taken to prevent roots and stems from coming into direct contact with the treated wood.

Garden Labels

Wooden labels, which are usually cut out from thin pieces of softwood, are liable to decay rapidly, and the thin coat of priming paint which they normally receive does little to prevent this. The value of nursery stock is seriously reduced if the labels distinguishing the varieties are lost, and it is well worth treating wooden labels by soaking them for about ten minutes in a copper naphthenate solution. Labels treated in this way can be painted white once the preservative has dried off.

Tool Handles

It is wiser not to treat tool handles, which may come into prolonged contact with the skin, with a toxic wood preservative. The best way to preserve them is to wipe them over once or twice a year with a rag soaked in linseed oil.

Miscellaneous

For the preservation of wooden sheds, the palings of fences, wooden slat fencing, and wooden wheelbarrows, regular (preferably annual) application of creosote, or other tar oil preservative, will ensure almost indefinite protection against decay. It is most important that the treatment be given when the timber is dry so as to ensure that any splits or shrinkage cracks are already open to absorb the preservative. It is also worth treating with creosote any wooden garden-bed or path edging boards, as these will decay very rapidly if they are set in the ground without treatment.

In the U.S.A. it has been found worth while treating wooden cases and crates used for gathering and transportation of fruit and vegetables. The preservative recommended for this is a water repellent formulation of cunilates (solubilised copper and quinolinolate compounds). This product renders the surface of wood resistant to mould but as it is quite insoluble and odourless it cannot contaminate the contents of the cases.

Fencing

There is probably no field of timber utilisation where wood preservation can be more usefully applied than for timber fencing. In spite of all that has been written on this subject there is still a great deal of untreated, or inadequately treated, wood used in fencing, and the general public still does not seem to appreciate the great economies that can result from the use of properly treated timber fencing. In the British Standard specification B.S. 1722 (revised) it is laid down that fencing timber shall receive preservative treatment unless a highly durable species of wood is used. Even where timbers such as European Oak, Sweet Chestnut, Larch, Yew, or Western Red Cedar are used preservation treatment is recommended if there is any sapwood present. Round poles from thinnings of these species always do, of course, contain sapwood, sometimes quite a high proportion of it. Too much faith is still placed in the natural durability of Oak and Larch, regardless of the amount of sapwood present.

Preparation of Timber

To obtain satisfactory treatment it is essential that the timber for posts and rails should first be seasoned so that there is no free water (or sap) filling the cell spaces—i.e. the cell spaces in the wood must be empty and open to receive the preservative. It is not necessary that the timber should always be fully air dried, but if it is to be treated with a water soluble preservative it should be dried down to a moisture content of about 30% (based on the oven dry weight), while material to be treated with creosote should be somewhat drier, about 25% or less. It is not possible to lay down hard and fast rules as to how long the drying must continue to achieve this as the time required depends on the weather, and on how much protection can be provided against the rain. Six weeks during the summer in East

Anglia may achieve more drying than six months during the winter in western Scotland!

It is important that all bark should be removed and that all necessary shaping, pointing or boring should be done before treatment. If for any reason timbers have to be cut after impregnation a preservative should be liberally applied by brush or spray to the cut surfaces, but no cutting at or below ground level, should ever be permitted after treatment.

Choice of Preservative and Method

Except when the fencing is to be painted, or where the smell of tar oils might be objectionable, creosote is the usual choice for fence posts. It is cheap, persistent, generally available, and can readily be applied by the hot and cold process. Pressure impregnation with creosote should be carried out in accordance with British Standards 913.

For the small user and the amateur gardener reasonably satisfactory treatment can be achieved by prolonged, i.e. several days, steeping, provided that the poles are well seasoned and are made of a permeable wood such as Pine, Elm, or Beech. They will probably not last so long as impregnated posts, but they will have a much longer life than if they had merely been brushed over with preservative.

Timber that has subsequently to be painted should be impregnated with a highly fixed water-borne preservative of the copper-chrome, or copper-chrome-arsenic type.

Impregnation of posts or rails by treatment in a cylinder gives the greatest protection; but for round posts very good penetration can be obtained by open tank treatment, provided that the timber is adequately seasoned. Butt treatment (see page 43) economises in the amount of preservative required and can give a greatly increased life. The amount of preservative that can be absorbed during simple brush treatment can never give lasting protection to timber that is to come in contact with the soil. Palings and boardings, however, that are accessible and can be retreated at intervals, can be effectively treated by brushing or spraying, at five yearly intervals, with a brushing quality of creosote. It is important that the wood should be quite dry when the creosote oil is applied.

PRESERVATION OF TIMBER IN BOATS, MARINE WORKS AND COOLING TOWERS

BOATS

WHEN all ships were built of timber, rot was a major hazard against which the old shipbuilders had no defence. Even the need to use seasoned timber, free from sapwood, was not properly understood, and the provision of any adequate ventilation to enclosed spaces was usually neglected. Ramsbottom and others have described the ravages wrought by decay in battleships during the Napoleonic wars. Apart from using naturally durable woods no successful method for protecting ships timbers was developed until the present century. The only preservative used to any extent in wooden ships was rock salt. This was packed around the timbers at certain vulnerable spots where leakage of water would dissolve the salt and 'pickle' the adjacent timber. This probably had some beneficial effect but sodium chloride is only mildly toxic to fungi and it accelerates the corrosion of metalwork.

During the second World War many wooden ships were built and, as was inevitable under wartime conditions, the materials with which they were made, and the workmanship put into them, were not always of such good quality as to ensure for them a long working life. After the war most of these vessels were either sold or put into reserve. A boat which is laid up or is used only at long intervals deteriorates very much more rapidly than one which is used regularly. For this reason many owners of yachts which had been laid up during the war found a considerable amount of decay when they came to refurbish them.

Much has been written about the reasons why decay develops in boats. Duff has pointed out that leakage of rainwater through the deck is a primary cause of decay in frames and in deck beams; and both he and Savory have emphasised the great importance of adequate ventilation to closed spaces such as the forepeak. It is undoubtedly extremely important to ensure that as little leakage of water as possible occurs, and that there is provision for ventilating all dead air spaces. At the same time it must be recognised that, with the working of a boat at sea, some joints inevitably open up, and also that not all owners look after their boats as well as they should do. Were it possible for all boats to be built by skilled shipwrights, out of naturally durable timbers such as Teak or Makoré, neglect would not have serious effects. But, unfortunately, many of the timbers, such as African Mahogany, which in all other respects are very suitable for boat building, are not highly resistant to decay. Fibre glass hulls made their appearance just at a time when many owners of wooden vessels were concerned about the risk of decay, and whatever their other virtues or defects, it can truthfully be claimed that they are proof against rot. The boat builder to-day has therefore an alternative to timber if he has reason to worry about the risk of decay, and so if he is to continue building with timber he must be convinced that this risk can be minimised.

Use of Naturally Durable Timbers

It is obviously easier for the boat builder to use naturally durable timbers, if these are available at a competitive price, than to have the trouble of treating a non-durable species, and it is legitimate to ask how far boat builders have made use of the durable species available. Many of these tend to be heavy and some are more difficult to work than the traditional ones used by shipwrights in the past, so that there has been a certain reluctance to experiment with some of the recently introduced durable varieties. Guarea and Makoré are two that might well be used more extensively for hull planking, and Agba would be suitable for deck beams etc. There is really no reason to use the relatively perishable imported American or Canadian Elm for frames when very much more durable homegrown Oak is available. Larch is another wood that has many advantages as it is resistant to soft rot as well as to ordinary wet rot, and to alkali attack arising from electro-chemical action. It could be used with great advantage for planking if adequate supplies of graded quality were available.

Preservative Treatment

Insufficient attention has been given to the use of wood preservatives on timber in boats due to the various difficulties involved. Pressure treatment, for instance, to be effective must be applied to a permeable timber in a seasoned condition and even then complete through and through penetration is seldom achieved with timbers of very large dimensions. This means that when the treated timber is recut and fashioned to the required shapes untreated wood in the core of the pieces may become exposed. Then again it must be recognised that boat builders tend to be conservative in their choice of timber and many of them would regard with suspicion a suggestion to use, for example, pressure treated Beech (a readily treatable wood) for stems or stern pieces, in place of the usual Oak.

Surface treatments have been used to a limited extent, but in many cases the quantity of preservative applied by brushing has been insufficient to afford really adequate protection. However effective a preservative may be it cannot indefinitely protect large-sized timbers if there is only a thin skin of treated wood on the surface. This is especially true if the preservative is in any degree volatile.

Despite the difficulties it is nowadays possible to give very useful preservative treatment to those timbers in ships that are particularly susceptible to decay. This is most likely to occur in timbers exposed to the damp conditions which result from intermittent leakage of fresh water, or from condensation in ill ventilated spaces. It has been shown by Savory and others that decay very commonly occurs in the ends of deck beams and the heads of frames, and in stringers, and so it is for these timbers that treatment is most necessary. In cabin cruisers decay not uncommonly occurs in the transom and in the framing of deck houses, so here again preservative treatment is well worth while. Wooden treenails should always be thoroughly soaked in preservative as their subsequent decay may have serious consequence.

Wood that is permanently saturated with water is not susceptible to ordinary fungal decay of the type commonly referred to as Dry Rot, but it may suffer the slow surface softening called Soft Rot. Marine anti-fouling paint has been found to give good protection against this.

Wood that is kept permanently dry does not rot and therefore it is unnecessary to treat the interior joinery and furniture in a boat.

Methods of Treatment

1. *Pressure Treatment.* In the United States pre-treatment by pressure impregnation has been given to timber laminae for large laminated frames in minesweepers and other naval craft. In this way really thorough impregnation of even very large sized members has been achieved. In this country, however, impregnation treatment does not appear to have been used to any significant extent in boat building either for solid or for laminated timbers.

The best treatment for laminae is impregnation with a copper chrome-arsenic mixture, after which they should be kiln dried down to a moisture content of 12-15%. They can then be satisfactorily glued together with resorcinol or phenol formaldehyde adhesives conforming to B.S. 1204. Any dust or surplus crystals of preservative on the surface should be brushed off before the glue is applied. In this way large-sized members such as the stem or keel can be built up from treated laminae.

Satisfactory as this method may be there are several difficulties in the way of its immediate development. For one thing the smaller boat builders are seldom equipped to carry out such a highly skilled operation, and for another those timbers at present most commonly used in boat building, Douglas Fir and Oak, are both very resistant to the penetration of liquids. There would, however, seem to be scope for considerably more use of impregnated plywood bonded according to B.S. 1088.

2. *Steeping and Brushing.* In so far as wood preservatives have been used in British boat yards they have generally been applied by brushing or spraying; less frequently by immersing the pieces in a bath of preservative. As already mentioned the failures that have occurred in timber treated in these ways can usually be attributed to the inadequate amounts of preservative applied. It is not enough merely to brush over the wood so that the surface becomes brown or green; there *must* be an appreciable penetration and absorption of the fluid into the wood. This can best be achieved by steeping the pieces in a solvent type preservative, after they have been fashioned to their final sizes

I

and all the necessary holes for bolts etc. have been drilled. When long pieces have to be treated it is sometimes difficult to find a tank long enough to accommodate them, and it may also be expensive to fill such a bath with preservative. Provided that there is sufficient headroom to operate a gantry, or block and tackle, these difficulties can be overcome by orientating the treating vessel vertically and immersing the pieces first one end and then the other. Another advantage of this system is that the hydrostatic pressure given by 8-10 ft. of liquid has a very beneficial effect in forcing the liquid into the exposed grain of the lower end of the piece.

A suitable vessel for steeping can fairly easily be made by rolling steel sheet into a tube of about 12 ins. diameter and welding the seams. The whole tube is then welded onto a steel base plate and provided with a drainage cock near the bottom. The tube can be supported by stout metal bands bolted onto brackets fixed to the walls of the shed.

The times of immersion will vary from a few minutes to several hours, according to the species of wood and the dimensions of the pieces to be treated. An immersion period of ten minutes will generally suffice for thin material, while a period of one hour may be required to achieve adequate absorption in material two to four inches thick. After the first few minutes the amount of preservative absorbed is roughly proportional to the square root of the time of immersion. There is, therefore, increasingly less advantage as the immersion period is prolonged. For example four hours immersion would be necessary to double the absorption that takes place in one hour.

For timbers that cannot be immersed in preservative on account of their size or shape, brushing with not less than three full flowing coats of preservative will afford quite a good measure of protection.

3. *Diffusion Treatments*. Though the treatment of timber by diffusion methods is a relatively new development, the same principle was long ago employed in the salt packing referred to above. One such method is the insertion of pellets of sodium pentachlorophenate into woodwork where there is leakage and signs of incipient decay. The idea of this is that any water entering through the leaks will carry with it an antiseptic in solution which will arrest the further spread of decay.

Bandages made of fabric containing preservative salts such as fluorides and dinitrophenol have been used for ground line treatment of poles—probably similar, but smaller bandages could be used with advantage for the protection of vulnerable spots in boats. They could, for instance, be applied to the ends of deck beams simply by tacking them closely onto the wood with the broad headed galvanised nails used for fixing roofing felt.

Boron preservatives, properly formulated to give neutral solutions, should also be very suitable for in-situ diffusion treatment of boat timbers. These could be applied, either as a paste or on thin bandages, to any vulnerable parts where leakage might be expected to occur.

When a hull is constructed of two layers of planking it is usual to place a layer of canvas soaked in linseed oil, or paint, between the two skins. This does not, however, prevent fungal growths that may have become established in one layer of planking from passing through into the other, but if an effective fungicide is added to the liquid in which the canvas is soaked then the spread of rot from one skin to another will be checked. Pentachlorophenol, at a concentration of about 4%, is the fungicide which has been most generally recommended for this purpose. In the United States it is common to use an adhesive, which they call 'double planking cement', between the two layers of planking. The addition of a fungicide to this adhesive has been recommended in a number of American publications.

4. *Bilge Treatments.* The idea of adding some antiseptic to the bilge water, which would be carried to any timbers wetted by splashing about of the water in the bilges, was first suggested in America, and Duff has since put it into practice in this country. Pentachlorophenol, suspended in nylon bags, was the first chemical to be used for this purpose, but, as it is soluble in water only to a very slight degree, a considerable time must elapse before sufficient preservative can be absorbed by the timbers to have any appreciative effect. Neutral solutions of boron compounds would seem well worth trying for this purpose as they are cheap, non-poisonous, and non-corrosive. A product containing boron, suitable for this purpose, has been marketed by a firm in this country. See Appendix.

Use of Plywood in Boats

When plywood was first used in boats there were discouraging cases of failure, but these were due to the use of unsuitable adhesives and of non-durable timbers. In the first edition of the British Standards for Plywood for Marine Craft (B.S. 1088), though suitable and durable glues based on phenol formaldehyde and resorcinol were specified, the choice of timber to be used for the veneers was left to the manufacturers and purchasers. In consequence some of the plywood sold as conforming to the specification was made either wholly of nondurable woods, or with a core of a perishable timber such as Obeche, with Mahogany face veneers. In the second edition of this specification suitable durable timbers are listed, but it is still not always easy to obtain plywood made of such timbers, and so preservative treatment may be called for. Plywood can be treated after manufacture in the same way as solid timber, but the most thorough treatment can be obtained by impregnating the veneers before they are bonded together. Plywood is now available in this country made up from timbers impregnated with copper-chrome and copper-chrome-arsenic preservatives, but so far boat builders do not appear to have used it very extensively.

MARINE WORKS

Marine piling, and other dock and harbour works, are exposed to two separate hazards. Firstly the portions above the water line are liable to ordinary fungal decay, and secondly the underwater portions and the intertidal zone may be attacked by Marine Borers. Recently it has been discovered that there are also marine micro-fungi that can cause Soft Rot in timber in the sea similar to that which occurs in cooling towers. This type of decay progresses very slowly but it appears to facilitate Gribble attack. In fact some investigators claim that Gribble can only attack wood after it has been infected with these fungi. Both the above-water and the under-water zones are exposed to severe leaching, so unless very durable timbers are used, such as Greenheart, Wallaba, or Turpentine, thorough preservation should be given. This should consist of full cell impregnation with a high retention of creosote, or a copper-chrome solution (with or without arsenic) at a retention of 0·5 lb. cub. ft. It is unfortunate that one of the most suitable timbers for piling, Douglas Fir, has a heartwood highly resistant to penetration. Most of the permeable sapwood has been cut away from the squared baulks that are shipped to this country, and, even after having been incised, prolonged treatment is necessary in order to get adequate penetration of preservative. If only engineers could be persuaded to accept round piling, which is very commonly used in America, adequate penetration of the necessary amounts of preservative could be obtained very much more easily.

COOLING TOWER TIMBERS

The older water cooling towers were constructed entirely of wood—a timber framework supported wooden cladding and the display areas of wooden louvres, or slats, over which the water flowed. Most modern towers consist of a concrete chimney the shape of an hour glass, which houses the display of wooden slats which may be supported on a wooden framework. After a few years the slats, which are either wedge shaped with $1\frac{1}{2}$ in. sides or flat $\frac{1}{2}$ in. thick battens, become softened on the surface and gradually get thinner until they eventually collapse. A very large volume of timber is required to fill one of these large towers and it may cost as much as £10,000 to replace the timbering. The life of the timber slats varies from twenty years down to as little as seven to ten years, depending on many factors including the nature of the circulating water and its content of impurities. It was thought at one time that the breakdown of the wood was the result of prolonged exposure to hot water. Microscopic examination of the decayed surface has since revealed that the fibres were permeated with the hyphae of fungi, and that the breakdown could be attributed to fungal decay of the type now known as Soft Rot. The wood is generally too wet for the growth of the ordinary wood-rotting Basidiomycete fungi, though occasionally species such as *Poria nigrescens*, which can tolerate very wet conditions, occur on the larger structural timbers.

Since the timber filling of a cooling tower is continuously washed with warm water only preservatives that are fixed to a very high degree have any chance of persisting for any length of time. Creosote is not considered suitable for treating slats as a proportion of the oil might possibly find its way into the condensers. Copper-chrome preservatives, with or without the addition of arsenic (e.g. Celcure or Tanalith C), have been found to give excellent protection for a number of years, provided that they are used in such a concentration as to give a final retention of about 125 lbs. per cub. ft. in the superficial zones of the timbers. Retentions of this order can generally be achieved by treating 'to refusal' in a 5% solution.

REFERENCES

Duff, M. G. 'Decay in Wood Built Boats', *Ship and Boat Builder*, **5**, 1951/2.

Ramsbottom, J. R. 'Dry Rot in Ships', *Essex Naturalist*, **25**, 231-67, 1937.

Ross, F. F., and Wood, M. J. 'The Preservation of Timber in Cooling Towers', *Brit. Wood Pres. Assoc. Convention Record*, p. 171, 1957.

Savory, J. G., and Packman, D. F. 'Prevention of Decay of Wood in Boats', *For. Prod. Res. Bull.*, **31**, 18pp. H.M.S.O., 1954.

CHAPTER X

PRESERVATION OF
POLES, RAILWAY SLEEPERS, MINING TIMBERS, VEHICLES, PACKING CASES, PLYWOOD, etc.

Poles

The preservation of wooden poles for telephone wires and transmission lines has been one of the major activities of the wood preserving industry, and a great deal of information is available about the service life of treated poles. For one instance, an international enquiry in Europe showed that the average life of creosoted telegraph poles was 26 years, while that of untreated poles, including many made of naturally durable woods such as Oak, Sweet Chestnut and Larch, was only $9\frac{1}{2}$ years.

In this country and the U.S.A. the only preservative used on a large scale for the treatment of poles has been creosote. It is generally applied by the Rueping, or Empty Cell Process, which gives a pole that is cleaner to handle, and less liable to 'bleed' creosote on the surface after erection, than one that has been treated by the full cell Bethell process. Complete penetration of the poles is not necessary and would, in fact, be wasteful of oil, as provided that the sapwood is fully impregnated the pole will be adequately protected. With Scots Pines this normally implies a ring of treated wood $1\frac{1}{2}$-2 ins. deep around the pole.

When poles are to be painted after treatment—e.g. to increase their visibility at night—or when it is desirable that the poles should not have an oily surface, they should be impregnated with a water-borne preservative, containing copper, that becomes fixed in the wood to a very high degree, such as Celcure A or Tanalith C.

The Cobra method of treatment (see page 45) is suitable for poles in areas that are remote from treating plants. It has also been used with considerable success for extending the life of poles that were inadequately treated in the first place and which have begun to suffer incipient decay though still retaining adequate strength.

One of the cheapest ways of preserving poles in temporary lines is to tack onto them, at ground level, bandages containing preservative salts. These are best put on before the poles are erected, but can be applied to standing poles if the soil is drawn away to a depth of 12 inches or so below the normal soil level before the bandage is fixed.

Railway Sleepers

It has long been standard practice in British railways to impregnate all sleepers under pressure with creosote by the full cell process. With pine sleepers that contain a fair proportion of sapwood overall retentions of 8-10 lbs. of creosote per cub. ft. are commonly obtained, and a minimum retention of 8 lbs./cub. ft. should be specified.

It is difficult to achieve adequate penetration into Douglas Fir and sleepers made with this wood should always be incised on all four faces before treatment so as to achieve side penetration of at least ¾ in. (See Pl. X, 1.)

All holes for fixings etc. must be bored before the timbers are impregnated.

Sleepers can also be effectively protected against decay by impregnation with well fixed water-borne preservatives, but they suffer more splitting than do those that have been impregnated with creosote oil and for this reason a supplementary treatment with an oil may be given to seal the timber and minimise splitting. Sleepers for tramways in underground mines should be treated with water-borne preservatives. (See next section.)

In countries where fuel oil is cheaper than creosote it can be used to replace a proportion of the creosote, up to about a third fuel oil to two-thirds creosote.

Mining Timbers

In a damp mine conditions are often ideal for fungal growth, in fact old underground workings have often been used for mushroom growing. Wood-rotting fungi will grow at a surprising rate when a high atmospheric pressure is combined with a temperature that is often just about the optimum for their growth. Under such conditions pit props of 5-6 inches

1. Decay in railway sleeper due to inadequate penetration of creosote
(Crown copyright)

2. Decay, due to inadequate penetration of preservative, in a pole
which had not been properly dried before treatment
(Crown copyright)

diameter may in one year become so severely decayed as to require replacement.

The props which support the roof at the coal face are only in use for a few weeks before they are withdrawn or abandoned, but the timbering of the main roads and shafts may be required to last many years. Apart from the risk of these timbers collapsing if they decay, the cost of their repeatedly having to be replaced must inevitably be considerable as it involves much labour, and over the years it will far exceed the cost of initial pre-treatment.

Prior to the war coal mining companies in this country showed little interest in wood preservation. When the timbers supporting the roofs along permanent roadways became unsafe they were generally replaced by steel arches. Nevertheless a considerable amount of timber is still used in mines for packing behind the steel arches and for sleepers.

Practical experiments carried out before the war by the Forest Products Research Laboratory, and more recently by the National Coal Board, have shown conclusively that a preservative treatment which adds no more than 30% to the initial cost of the timber itself can extend its life from a few months up to ten years or longer. Hollingsworth, as a result of his studies in this field, concluded that 'there is a proven, if limited, field for mining-timber preservation . . . which promises increased safety and valuable economies'.

In South Africa the Transvaal Chamber of Mines has established a well equipped research laboratory for the study of problems relating to the preservation of mining timbers, and valuable economies in the use of timber have resulted from the investigations carried out there.

Where the timbers used are of small diameter and consist mainly of sapwood satisfactory absorptions of preservatives can be obtained by the open tank process. This type of plant which is relatively cheap to erect and operate, can be installed at the pit head. When the timber is of a species that is resistant to penetration, impregnation under pressure in a cylinder will give better protection, and of course a much larger through-put of timber can be achieved in a pressure plant. In this country such plants are generally operated by treating companies who contract to impregnate the timber needed by the mines.

The essential features of a preservative to be used on timber in underground workings are the following:

1. It must give effective protection against fungal decay. (Insects are of little importance underground.)
2. It must not increase the flammability of the wood, nor give off poisonous fumes if ignited.
3. It should not render the wood unpleasant to handle.
4. It should be cheap.

Tar oils are not generally liked and solvent type preservatives can be ruled out on account of their high cost as well as their flammability. Water-borne preservatives are usually chosen because they can readily be combined with fire retardant chemicals, and adequate protection can be provided with solutions of low cost.

A great deal of mining timber in Europe has been successfully treated with various mixtures of the Wolman salts type, containing sodium fluoride, sodium chromate, and dinitrophenol. Experiments in this country have shown that impregnation with 2% solutions of sodium fluoride and zinc chloride can also give quite effective protection. In very few mines is there so much free water that leaching out of the salts becomes serious so it is rarely necessary to use highly fixed water-borne salts. A 2% boric/borax mixture should prove very effective and would probably provide the cheapest solution for the preservation of timber.

Vehicles

When the bodywork of motor cars was largely made of wood it was quite usual, especially in the tropics, for serious decay to occur before the vehicle had worn out mechanically. With the advent of the pressed steel body corrosion of the metal is now the major cause of the deterioration of bodywork. Nevertheless a certain amount of wood is still used for fixing pieces for the upholstery etc. and this should be treated by immersion in a solvent type preservative, particularly if the vehicle is to be exported to the tropics.

In Great Britain there has been more trouble with decay in public service vehicles and lorries than in private cars. To-day caravans are probably the type of vehicle that stand in the greatest need of preservative treatment for several reasons:

1. They are often built of light non-durable woods, and of plywood that may be resistant to delamination under damp conditions but not to rot.
2. They are left to stand out in the open in all weathers.
3. They often suffer heavy condensation of moisture on the walls and roof from cooking and washing operations.

All the wooden members, after being fashioned to their final size, should be immersed for ten minutes in a bath of a solvent type preservative containing a water repellent. (See Appendix.) All the joints should be bedded with a sealing compound that does not become brittle with age. All the plywood should be of exterior quality bonded with a synthetic resin adhesive, and in addition it should be given two generously brushed-on coats of a solvent type preservative on both faces and all the edges.

Packing Cases

Normally packing cases do not require preservation as they are scrapped after a single journey. They are, however, certain returnable cases, such as those used for bottled beer, which are expected to last for a long time. These are usually given a coat of varnish, which improves their appearance, but probably a dip in a water repellent preservative would give greater and more lasting protection.

Then there is the question of military stores which often have to be stored for long periods under highly unfavourable conditions, such as exist in old underground workings, disused mines and so forth. During the second World War large quantities of stores became useless in New Guinea and in Burma owing to the rotting of their containers. It was then laid down that all wooden ammunition boxes and cases for other military stores should be given preservative treatment. Two methods were used; either impregnation with a well fixed water-borne preservative, or dipping treatment in solvent type preservative. When the former method is used it is absolutely essential that the timber should be re-dried after treatment; otherwise severe corrosion of the contents may result from the moisture left in the timber. If metal stores are to be packed in treated wooden cases it is, of course, essential that no ingredient in the preservative should induce or accelerate corrosion of the stores themselves. For this reason it is most important that the treating solution should be neutral in reaction and contain no free acid.

Probably waterproof plywood, impregnated with preservative during manufacture, is one of the most suitable materials for high class packing cases that are required to be completely resistant to insect and fungal attack. Unfortunately it is a relatively expensive material. Fibre boards of high wet strength are now available from which containers can be made that will withstand quite long periods of exposure to damp conditions.

Plywood

Prior to the discovery of waterproof glues there was little interest in the preservation of plywood against decay, because material bonded with protein glues (hide, blood or casein) would, in any case, under persistently damp conditions, become useless through delamination. In Australia the treatment of veneers cut from *Lyctus*-susceptible hardwoods with boric acid solutions was established before the second World War and is now quite a standard practice. Tamblyn and others have shown that dip diffusion treatment of the green veneers in strong solutions of borax can result in sufficient absorptions of preservative to give good protection of the plywood to insects and fungi. Plywood can also be rendered resistant to insect attack by incorporating a small proportion of a chlorinated insecticide in the glue, and it is now common practice in New Zealand to put 0·3% dieldrin in plywood glues, this proportion being based on the made up glues.

When making plywood with veneers that have been treated with preservative it is extremely important to use a glue that will be compatible with the preservative. Provided that the appropriate glue is used and the makers' instructions are followed closely the bond strength of the joints need not be appreciably reduced by the presence of the preservative. The moisture content of the veneers should be between 11% and 14% at the time of glueing and the surfaces of the wood should be quite clean. It has been shown that the bond strength of plywood made with veneers treated with polyborate and copper-chrome-arsenate preservatives and bonded with urea formaldehyde and resorcinol formaldehyde glues was not significantly different from that of plywood made with untreated veneers.

Plywood manufactured from veneers pre-treated with Celcure or Tanalith C preservative is now commercially available in this country.

As an alternative to treatment during manufacture plywood can be treated on the site by brushing all the surfaces, not forgetting the edges, with a preservative; but the degree of protection given by surface treatment cannot, of course, equal that afforded by impregnation. It is possible to achieve through and through penetration of thin plywood by pressure impregnation in a cylinder, but it is difficult to treat large sheets in this way, and it is more efficient to apply the preservative during manufacture.

There would appear to be scope for a considerable increase in the use of preserved plywood, for instance in boat building and for the construction of sheds, but so far its rather high price has restricted its use.

Composite Materials

Wall boards are not normally used in very damp situations where there is a risk of fungal decay so the question of their preservation against rot does not often arise. However in countries where termites are a menace it may be desirable to give such materials some protection against insect attack. The addition to chipboard of 3% boric acid, or 2% boric acid plus 0.5% sodium pentachlorophenate, has given very promising results. These figures are based on the oven dry weight of wood in the board.

Probably the most important treatments that are applied to insulating board are those designed to reduce the flammability of the material. The fire retardant chemicals referred to on page 145 can be introduced into wall boards, during or after manufacture, and will give the material greatly increased fire resistance.

CHAPTER XI

PRESERVATION OF WOODEN ANTIQUES

WHEN wooden objects are received by a museum or when they are collected during archaeological excavations they are often in a very fragile condition. However with appropriate treatment they may be greatly strengthened and preserved for display or for further study. Broadly speaking they fall into two classes—firstly objects such as furniture or carvings which have been kept under comparatively dry conditions but which are often more or less seriously weakened by woodworm; and secondly objects discovered in the soil or under water which are in a saturated condition. These two types of material require entirely different treatment if they are to be conserved to the best advantage.

Treatment of Dry Objects

On receiving any wooden object it should be carefully examined for signs of insect attack. If any exit holes or tunnnels are found an effort should be made to discover if there is any active infestation by a careful search for piles of bore dust and for fresh exit holes. Before any attempt is made to consolidate the wood any live insects present must be killed; but it is not always easy to determine whether an active infestation is present and if there is any doubt it is wiser to give the material an insecticidal treatment.

This can be done in several ways, e.g. by heating, by fumigating, or by treatment with a liquid insecticide.

Heat treatment must be given with considerable caution, as heating will tend to dry out the wood and may cause it to shrink and split. In any case the temperature should never exceed about 140°F, and the atmosphere should be kept humid.

Fumigation with a poisonous gas requires the use of a specially sealed gas chamber and should only be undertaken by properly qualified staff as some of the gases used are as deadly to man as they are to insects.

Insecticidal liquids that give off fumes which are toxic to insects are more convenient to use. Dr Plenderleith recommends carbon disulphide for fumigation of valuable objects as it does not harm delicate materials. The method he recommends is as follows:

The infested material is placed in a box or vessel that can be tightly closed and sealed, and above it flat glass dishes containing the carbon disulphide are placed, about one ounce of the liquid being used for 8 cubic ft. of space. Depending on the thickness of the objects to be treated they should be kept in the fumigation box for 2-3 weeks, the carbon disulphide being replaced after each week if it has all evaporated. The vapour of this chemical is explosive when mixed with air and so care must be taken to avoid naked lights or smoking in a room where it is being used. After the treatment the object should be exposed to the air to get rid of the fumes.

By fumigation it is possible to sterilise wood without altering its appearance in any way, but of course no residual insecticide remains to protect the material against the possible risk of reinfestation at a later date.

Liquid insecticides containing dieldrin or BHC (gammexane) in suitable non-staining solvents, are available commercially and it is probably wiser to use one of these specially formulated products than to attempt to prepare home-made mixtures. Since the quantities of liquid required are not likely to be great there will be no worth while saving in cost by making it up at home. The insecticide should be injected into the exit holes in any painted surfaces, and brushed freely and repeatedly over rough surfaces where unpainted or unvarnished wood is exposed. After all the solvent has evaporated the holes and small cavities should be filled with a soft wax such as beeswax, appropriately coloured to match the wood. Insecticidal waxes are available containing a chemical that is toxic to insects, and these will give some extra protection against re-infestation.

Consolidation of Weakened Wood

After any active infestation has been dealt with by fumigation, or by treatment with a liquid insecticide, softened or seriously weakened articles will need to be consolidated.

Large objects that are seriously weakened may require some mechanical reinforcement with wooden dowels or splints. If any plywood is used it should be 'exterior grade', bonded with a synthetic resign and not with a protein glue. Large cavities can most conveniently be filled by shaping a piece of Balsa wood roughly to fit the cavity and embedding it with a resin. Alternatively the cavity may be filled with a paste made of sawdust, of a wood similar to that of the object, mixed with glue.

After the necessary mechanical repairs have been effected the whole object may be impregnated with a material that will set hard after it has permeated the decomposed wood. Waxes have long been used for this purpose, generally beeswax, containing a proportion of resin not exceeding 50%. The object to be treated, which must be thoroughly dry and free from dust, is immersed in a tank containing the molten wax which is heated up to 220°F (105°C). As the air in the pores of the wood becomes hot it expands and bubbles out making way for the molten wax to penetrate. It is safer not to heat the bath containing the wax over a naked flame as any liquid wax splashed over might ignite and cause a serious fire. If an appreciable number of articles have to be treated it is worth while installing an electrically heated bath with thermostatic control of the temperature.

Wax treatment affords considerable protection against damp, but it has the disadvantage that it may alter the tone of the colours, and also that the wax may bleed out of the wood if the treated objects are subsequently exposed to the sun. For these reasons it may be thought preferable to use a solution of a synthetic resin—e.g. polyvinyl acetate dissolved in 9 parts of toleuene and 1 part of acetone. There are now a number of proprietary preparations of synthetic resins specifically formulated for the treatment of antique wood. Some of these contain insecticidal chemicals in addition to a hardening resin.

In order to facilitate the penetration of the resin solution the impregnation is most effectively carried out in a closed chamber, from which the air can be withdrawn as in a pressure treating cylinder (see page 38). Small objects can be treated in an ordinary laboratory vacuum desiccator.

Wet and Waterlogged Wood

Many specimens of wood of archaeological interest, which have been discovered during excavations, appear at first sight to be relatively undamaged. But if these are allowed to dry out quickly they may shrink excessively and even collapse entirely. The reason for this is that much of the cellulose, of which the wood was originally largely composed, has been decomposed during the centuries as a result of slow fungal and bacterial attack. The lignin fraction of the wood, which resists such decomposition, persists, but it has little tensile strength once the water in the cells has been withdrawn. It is therefore essential to keep any wooden objects, discovered during excavations, in a thoroughly wet condition, at least until they have been carefully examined and photographed in the laboratory.

Immediately after collection the specimens should be packed, on the site, in wet moss or cotton wool, and wrapped in waterproof film. If they are fairly small they can be preserved indefinitely in the laboratory if they are put under water containing a trace of antiseptic such as carbolic acid.

If it is wished to display a specimen it becomes necessary to dry it, and the difficult problem arises how to do this without the wood collapsing. Direct freeze drying is a method that has been used very successfully on fragile biological materials such as toadstools which shrink on drying. Rosenquist found it to give promising results and in his paper he gives a schematic drawing of suitable apparatus for the evaporation of ice under vacuum from frozen material. Organ, however, found it to be too unreliable for the very ancient material with which he had to deal.

Small objects can be treated by a technique familiar to histologists which consists in replacing the water in the wood by alcohol (ethanol), and then replacing the alcohol by ether, or xylene, containing a resin or wax in solution. The treatment is carried out in a series of steps in which the solutions are changed gradually. The following is a typical series:

Bath 1. 25% alcohol, 75% water
  „ 2. 50%   „   50%   „
  „ 3. 75%   „   25%   „
  „ 4. 95%   „   5%   „
  „ 5. 95%   „   5%   „
  „ 6. 50%   „   50% ether
  „ 7. 100% ether
  „ 8. 100% ether
  „ 9. Ether containing dammar resin.

K

The time spent in each bath will depend on the size of the specimen, but about one day for each half inch in length is suggested as the minimum. The volume of liquid in the bath should be at least five times that of the specimens being treated.

If it is wished to reduce the colour of the wood it may be bleached before treatment by immersion for a week in 5% hydrogen peroxide.

Such treatment is usually only given to fairly small objects as the materials used are expensive, volatile and flammable.

For consolidating larger pieces of wet wood the method known as the alum process has been used for over fifty years with considerable success. Alum (potassium aluminium sulphate) is a salt that is extremely soluble in hot water but only moderately so in cold. If wood is soaked for sufficiently long in a saturated solution of the salt at 212°F (100°C) it becomes charged with the salt which is deposited as a solid when the wood is cooled and then dried. The presence of the salt in such quantity prevents shrinkage and helps to consolidate the wood. Plenderleith recommends a solution made up with 2-3 parts by weight of potash alum in one part of boiling water plus one part of glycerine. The immersion time that he suggests is 10-30 hours depending on the size of the specimens to be treated. After treatment the specimens are quickly washed with water and allowed to cool and dry out. Any salts which may crystallise out afterwards on the surface should be brushed off. When the wood is quite dry its surface can be sealed with a mixture of turpentine and linseed oil, or else laquered.

The use of substances other than alum for replacing water in old wood has been explored by Rosenquist. She found that polyethelene glycol effectively preserved many of the coarser implements found in the Viking ship of Oseberg.

Organ has reported very successful preservation of Palaeolithic wooden objects recovered from a peaty clay by impregnation with a polythelene glycol known as Carbowax 4000. This has a melting point about 122°-140°F (about 50°-55°C) and is very soluble (though with some difficulty) in water. The method used was to stand the specimens in a strong solution of carbowax (1 part of wax in 5 of water) in a closed but not sealed vessel which was kept at first at about 80°F (30°C). The temperature was then raised at intervals till after a month it reached 140°F (about 60°C). When all the water had evaporated the specimens were impregnated with the wax. They were then removed, allowed to cool and any surplus wax washed off the surface with toluene. Organ pointed out in a later note that this method was not suitable for treating objects which, though waterlogged, still preserved considerable mechanical strength.

Another product that can be used directly on wet wood is water soluble methyl cellulose (which is sold as an adhesive for wall paper) used in increasing strengths, each coat being allowed to soak in and dry slowly before another is applied.

Trimethyl carbinol (tertiary butyl alcohol), which is very soluble in water as well as in many other solvents, has also been used with success for replacing the water in frozen wood. After this treatment the dried wood can be strengthened by impregnation with a plastic that solidifies in the wood, such as a solution of polymethylmethacrylate in benzene.

Biek *et al*, have described the successful restoration of a thirteenth-century wooden bucket by immersion of the staves in a urea formaldehyde resin solution. The pieces of wood were impregnated under vacuum with the solution for 12 hours, and were then submerged in a bath of the accelerator (hardener) for 30 minutes. After this they were washed quickly and wiped dry, and then placed in an oven kept between 90° and 100° until the resin had set hard. Any tendency of the staves to warp during this process was restrained by clamping them in preformed plywood moulds.

Müller-Beck and Hass (1960) set out the requirements of the ideal conservation method for ancient wood, and concluded that a water soluble synthetic resin, which would polymerise during evaporation, would be the answer. This they seem to have found in a product known as Arigal C, which was developed as a rot-proofing agent for cotton textiles. It is a melamine formaldehyde condensation product of unlimited water solubility, and is said to cost about 12-15 Swiss francs a kilo. The method they used for applying it was, briefly, as follows:

1. Wash the object in flowing water for three days.
2. Steep in 25% Arigal C, using five times the weight of solution to the weight of wood, occasionally heating gently

to 60°C to assist penetration, until the object sinks in the solution.

3. Remove the impregnated wood and place it in a bath containing a 10% solution of the appropriate catalyst. Put the bath in a vacuum container and reduce the pressure to 80 mm of mercury to remove any air bubbles. When the bubbles stop coming out release the pressure and leave the object in the solution for 35-40 hrs.

4. Wash quickly, wrap in a damp cloth, put it in a tightly sealed polythene bag, and heat at 149°F (65°C) for 48 hrs.

5. Remove object from wrappings and dry off gently at a temperature not higher than 95°-104°F (35°-40°C). Then leave in a room to finish drying out.

Müller-Beck and Hass claim to have achieved strikingly successful results by this process, which is much cheaper and less laborious than the ether method, and has the further advantage of not involving the use of flammable liquids. The articles which they treated in this way shrank very little and were strong and durable after the treatment.

Heavy Waterlogged Timbers

The preservation of really large objects such as dug-out canoes presents especial difficulties since they cannot easily be impregnated with any solution. It is generally recommended that, after they have been washed free from mud, they should be lifted onto a cradle or stretcher, and covered with a good thick layer of damp sand, or friable soil, and then left for a year or two for the water to drain out of the wood. The soil should then be judiciously removed and the object left to dry as slowly as possible in a place which, at least during the first stages of drying, is sheltered from the sun and wind and protected from frost.

When the surface has begun to dry it should be painted with a dilute solution of waterglass. If a disfiguring growth of mildew should appear on the surface of the wood while it is drying it should be sprayed with a 1.0% solution of sodium pentachlorophenate.

Less bulky objects have been successfully preserved against the development of surface cracking by submerging them, after thorough washing, in a tank of dilute glycerine, refilled at intervals as the water evaporates slowly from the surface of the mixed fluids. After a couple of years, by which time the glycerine concentration will have greatly increased, the timbers are removed and allowed to dry naturally for a further year. After this the surface can be coated with shellac.

To sum up—ancient waterlogged wood must be kept in a wet condition either until some conservation treatment is applied or, in the case of exceptionally bulky material, until arrangements can be made for it to dry out very slowly under cover.

REFERENCES

Biek, L., Anstee, J. W., and Cripps, E. S. 'A Wooden Bucket Restored', *Museum J.*, **57**, p. 257, 1958.

Müller-Beck, H., and Hass H. 'A Method for Wood Preservation using Arigal C, *Studies in Conservation*, **5** (4), p. 150, 1960.

Organ, R. M. 'Carbowax and Other Materials in the Treatment of Waterlogged Paleolithic Wood', *Studies in Conservation*, **4** (3), p. 96, 1959; **5** (4), p. 161, 1960.

Plenderleith, H. J. *The Conservation of Antiquities and Works of Art*, Oxford, 1956.

Rosenquist, A. M. 'Stabilizing of Wood Found in the Viking Ship of Oseberg', *Studies in Conservation*, **4** (1), p. 13, and (2), p. 62, 1959.

CHAPTER XII

PROTECTING LOGS AND LUMBER DURING SEASONING

So long as a tree stands with its bark intact and its roots in a healthy condition it will remain sound and free from decay. If, however, it should suffer wounds through the breaking or cutting off of large branches so that the heartwood becomes exposed to air-borne infection, then wood-rotting fungi may become established and cause heart rot in the standing trees. This rot may progress slowly within the tree for many years and remain undetected until the tree is felled. As the fungus attack is usually confined to the dead tissues the tree often continues to grow vigorously, and may show no external sign of the presence of rot in the heartwood. Similarly fungi may gain entry to the trunk through diseased roots and spread up into the central heartwood causing butt rot.

The protection of standing timber against infection is an important aspect of forest management, and as such really falls outside the scope of this book. Briefly, it involves attempting to grow trees so that they do not form large overhanging side branches which are liable to break off in storms; and also minimising the possibility of man-made wounds to the trunks occurring during forestry operations. In gardens or parkland it may be possible to protect such wounds by coating the exposed wood with an antiseptic wound dressing or with paint, but under forest conditions this is usually impracticable. It has however been found that the spread of butt rot caused by *Fomes annosus* within plantations can be checked by creosoting the stumps immediately the trees have been felled during thinning operations. This prevents the stumps from becoming centres of infection which may spread to the standing trees.

When a tree is felled the ends of the logs are immediately exposed to infection, and if the weather is warm the sapwood soon becomes discoloured by the growth of fast growing moulds which cause sapstain. A little later the wood-rotting fungi become established and incipient decay (dote) spreads in from the ends of the logs, as well as through branch stubs, and from any places where the bark has been torn off during logging operations. The logs are also likely to become infested by bark boring beetles and Pinhole Borers. In the temperate zone there are few insects on the wing during the winter so there is very little risk of insect attack during the winter months, but in the tropics the logs may be attacked within a few days after felling. Many of these bark beetles are associated with sap-staining moulds which gain entry into the logs through the punctures made by the insects. So to prevent logs from deteriorating between the time of felling and their conversion at the saw mill, measures must be taken to protect them against infestation by insects as well as against fungi.

The rate at which deterioration of logs takes place depends on three things:

1. The kind of timber involved.

2. The weather at the time of felling.

3. Prevalence of fungi and insect pests in the vicinity of the felled logs.

All except the most durable timbers will deteriorate if left indefinitely on the ground after felling but it is those species that contain a high proportion of sapwood, and those listed as perishable in Table 1 in which no durable heartwood is formed, that are most difficult to extract without their suffering degrade.

In countries where the winter is cold and temperatures below freezing point persist for months, logs of perishable species, such as Birch and Aspen, can be felled and left in the woods with no risk of their deteriorating until the warm weather returns. Even in Great Britain there is little risk of any fungal infection to such logs between mid-November and mid-March. But the fact that the timber is 'winter felled' does not, as some people seem to think, make it inherently any more durable than if it were felled in the summer. Winter felled logs of Beech, for instance, will deteriorate quickly if left lying in the woods during the warmer months of the year—a fact that many timber merchants learnt to their cost during the last war when transport difficulties led to delay in getting the logs out of the woods.

It is highly desirable that the logs of perishable species should not only be removed from the woods before the end of the cold weather, but that they should be sawn up without delay, and then piled openly to season. It may be necessary, however, to keep the sawmills supplied with logs throughout the year; pulp mills, for instance, must obviously hold several months supply of timber; and these stocks must be protected in some way or they will suffer serious deterioration.

PROTECTION OF LOGS

Water Storage

The best way to store logs awaiting conversion is to submerge them under water. So long as they are completely submerged they will remain free from insect attack and fungal decay, nor will there be any risk of the ends drying out causing deep splits to develop. But if any portion of a log is above the water level it may become stained or even decayed. To prevent this some log ponds are provided with transverse girders set in the walls at normal water level. By temporarily lowering the water level the logs can be floated under the girders which will then keep them fully submerged when the level is again raised.

When logs are held in rivers or natural lakes that have a soft muddy bottom there may be a risk of losing those that become waterlogged and sink, so suitable marker tags should be attached to valuable logs under such conditions.

In areas where Teredo Borers are active they may damage logs held in brackish water at the mouth of a river, but these pests cannot survive for long in fresh water.

Sawmills which do not possess a special log pond, or other area of water suitable for log storage, can nevertheless make use of water for the protection of perishable logs. This is done by spraying the piles of logs with a fine 'rain' from sprinklers of the type used for overhead irrigation. It is not necessary to use large volumes of water, but continuous rather than inter-mittent spraying is likely to give the better protection. A 'rain-fall' of half an inch per hour has been suggested as sufficient to protect logs during the summer months in Sweden. A growth of green algae over the ends of the logs is said to indicate that sufficient water is being supplied to inhibit decay.

1. Small hand-operated dipping tank, used for dipping Ramin in Sarawak

2. A small, partly mechanised dip. Timber arrives on rollers (seen on far side), is dropped on to chains and comes out on the nearside draining board

Chemical Protection

If water storage is not available, and delay in extraction and conversion is unavoidable, the cut ends, and any other exposed wood such as branch stubs and bark scrapes, should be brushed over with creosote or some other fungicide. This should be done immediately after felling and cross cutting, as it is useless to apply any superficial treatment once infection has penetrated even half an inch into the wood. Logs of hardwoods, such as Beech, are liable to split on drying out, thus exposing untreated wood in the cracks, and so a moisture retardant end-coating, as well as a fungicide, must be applied to the log ends and branch stubs. For example if Beech logs in this country have to be kept in the round after March, the ends and the other exposed areas should be swabbed freely, immediately after cutting, with 5% sodium pentachlorophenate solution, and then coated with a thick bituminous endcoating. Logs thus treated will be in far better condition than untreated ones after six months exposure on the ground.

In the tropics, and to a lesser degree in the temperate countries, logs may be attacked soon after felling by various kinds of beetle, notably Ambrosia Beetles (Pinhole Borers), which tunnel into the wood, often introducing the spores of staining fungi. For protecting logs against such infestation preparations containing benzene hexachloride (BHC) have been outstandingly successful. There are now commercially available water miscible formulations of this chemical which, after drying, form a water resistant film over the logs. If these products are properly applied, so as thoroughly to wet the whole surface of the log, they will effectively protect even susceptible timbers for many weeks. The amount of solution required effectively to protect a log will depend to a considerable extent on the efficiency with which the treatment is carried out. It is only too easy to waste chemicals by careless application. In the U.S.A. it has been estimated that about 2 gallons of solution should be sufficient to treat 100 sq. ft. of log surface.

PROTECTION OF SAWN TIMBER

Lumber (sawn timber) should be piled openly to season as soon as possible after it has been sawn. If untreated lumber is left in solid piles for even a few days in warm weather it will rapidly become stained, and even lumber that has been dipped can be left piled solid safely only for a matter of weeks.

The seasoning yard should be in open well-drained land over which air can move freely. It should be free from tall growing weeds and from off-cuts, sawdust and other woody waste in which fungi and pests can breed.

The lumber should be piled on solid foundations well off the ground, in stacks not more than 6 ft. wide, which should not be too close together. Some form of sloping roof, with an overhang of about 2 ft. at the lower end, should be provided to throw off rain water. Each layer of boards or planks should be separated by narrow, clean, dry piling sticks, carefully aligned one above the other in the vertical direction. Sticks one inch thick are generally used for softwoods, but for hardwoods, in good drying weather, half-inch thick sticks are more suitable so as to prevent unduly rapid drying with consequent splitting.

In Northern European countries, where the conversion of logs can be carried on during the colder periods, there is less risk of the sawn timber becoming infected before it has had time to season, than there is in warmer countries where milling operations must continue throughout the year. It is usually possible to season timber before wood-rotting fungi become established, but during warm damp weather moulds that cause sapstain can develop very quickly on some kinds of sawn timber, even if the pieces are piled quite openly. Under such conditions susceptible light coloured woods, such as Ramin and Obeche, must be given chemical treatment immediately after they have been sawn up in order to prevent them from becoming stained. A wide variety of chemicals has been tried for this purpose, but to-day sodium pentachlorophenate (NaPCP), with or without the addition of borax, is by far the most widely used. In general higher concentrations are required for protecting hardwoods in the tropics than for coniferous wood under cool temperate conditions. Concentrations of sapstain chemicals are generally expressed as lbs. of the commercial product to be mixed in 100 gallons of water. The range of recommended concentrations is as follows:

Conditions		Chemical	Concentration lbs./100 gallons
Average temperate		NaPCP	7 to 10
	or	NaPCP 1 part ⎫ Borax 3 parts ⎭	20
Tropical		NaPCP	20
	or	NaPCP 1 part ⎫ Borax 2 parts ⎭	30
Severe tropical		NaPCP 1 part ⎫ Borax 1 part ⎭	30

If it is desired to protect the sawn timber against subsequent infestation of Powder Post Beetle, 5 gallons of BHC emulsion should be mixed with 95 gallons of water containing the anti-stain chemicals.

The sawn timber is most effectively treated by dipping it for a few seconds in a bath of the antiseptic solution. In large mills this is done mechanically by passing the pieces by means of chains through a V-shaped trough. In small mills the pieces can be dipped by hand by operatives wearing stout rubber gloves. A wide drainage board should always be provided beside the dipping tank so that excess fluid can drain off the boards and back into the tank. (See Pl. XII, 1 and 2.)

Baulks of timber that are too heavy to pass through a dipping tank can be sprayed with the solution; but it is difficult to wet all the surfaces by hand spraying and, if a large volume of such wood is to be treated, arrangements should be made to pass the baulks through a proper, hooded, spray chamber in which jets of fluid are sprayed on to all the faces as the timber is moved through.

Effective prevention of sapstain and insect attack depends on careful control of the dipping treatments and attention to general hygiene in the timber yard.

It must be clearly understood that the momentary dipping treatments in comparatively weak solutions of fungicides, such as those described above, cannot give long lasting protection against decay, and should not be regarded as preservative treatment in the ordinary sense. They are intended only to protect lumber against deterioration during the seasoning period.

Failures of these treatments may result from any of the following causes:

1. The logs being already infected with stain. If boards already contain traces of the staining fungi when they are dipped the infection may develop later and cause internal stain even though the surfaces remain clean.
2. Exposure of the timber after treatment to heavy rain. This may dilute the chemicals so much that they no longer control the fungi.
3. Failure to control the concentration of chemicals in the dipping bath.
4. Undue delay in stacking the timber after it has been dipped.

Cost of Dipping Treatment

The chemicals used for making up anti-stain solutions are relatively cheap and the cost per gallon in this country should not exceed about fourpence. Providing there are proper arrangements for collecting the solution that drips off the boards after treatment, about 15 gallons of solution will be required to treat 1000 board ft. of one-inch boards. The absorption will be greater on rough sawn than on smooth sawn lumber. The labour costs involved will, of course, depend greatly on the layout and organisation of the yard. It has been estimated that the cost of labour in dipping 1000 board ft. may be between a tenth and an eighth of a day's wages.

Preparation of Timber for Treatment

Before any treatments, other than those involving diffusion, are applied it is highly desirable that the timber should be properly seasoned. This is for the simple reason that as long as the cells of the wood are filled with sap or water there is no room for the preservative oil or solution to enter. It is not necessary to dry the wood out completely because once the free water present in the cell spaces has gone, that is when the wood has dried down to its fibre saturation point, further drying will not appreciably increase the permeability of the wood or the amount of preservative that it can absorb.

It is extremely important that any cutting, boring or machining operations which the finished wooden article, be it sleeper, pole or joist, has to undergo, should be carried out before preservative treatment is given. There are two reasons for this. Firstly, any cutting into the wood after it has been treated may expose untreated wood in the core of the piece to infection, and secondly any holes that are made in the wood before it is treated provide useful ports of entry through which the preservative can enter the wood.

Satisfactory penetration to an adequate depth cannot be obtained in most grades of Douglas Fir, which are extremely resistant to impregnation, without prior incision of the timber. The incising process can also be used with considerable advantage in a number of other resistant species. Slits are made on all the surfaces of the wood about $\frac{1}{2}$ in. long, $\frac{1}{8}$ in. wide, and $\frac{1}{2}$-$\frac{3}{4}$ in. deep. This is done by passing the squared timbers through four revolving steel rollers fitted with teeth spaced so as to give the desired pattern of holes. The spacing of the incisions is adjusted so that the preservative spreading out from them along the grain permeates the entire zone of the wood to the depth of the incisions.

If for any reason it becomes necessary to do any cutting or boring after the timbers have been impregnated the unprotected wood thereby exposed should be swabbed repeatedly with preservative. End cuts can be treated in this way fairly effectively, but it is very difficult to obtain adequate penetration on side cut surfaces by any superficial treatment.

CHAPTER XIII

FIRE RETARDANT TREATMENTS

EVERY year hundreds of lives are lost, and millions of pounds' worth of damage is brought about, as the result of fires in buildings. In 1959 the losses due to fire reached the staggering total of £44,000,000, and nearly 700 people lost their lives. Though the source of such fires can be traced, more often than not, to the ignition of combustible material, or furniture stored in the building, any structural or decorative woodwork that forms part of the building itself soon becomes involved and contributes to the spread of the flames.

Timbers vary greatly in the ease with which they can be ignited, and in the rate at which they will burn. In general dense, heavy hardwoods are more resistant to burning than light, resinous softwoods; and certain timbers, such as Greenheart, Gurjun, Jarrah, Iroko, Oak, Padauk, and Teak, are classified as very resistant to fire, and their use for making fire resistant doors has been officially approved.

The resistance to fire of timber and of wood products can be greatly increased by treatment with certain chemicals. It is, however, a mistake to call such treatments 'fire proofing'. No treatment can render timber immune to all the effects of high temperatures. When wood is exposed to a high temperature the process known as destructive distillation begins, and flammable gases are given off. Between 300° and 400° F the wood scorches and then the flammable gases begin to come off. As the temperature rises above 400° the wood chars and the evolution of the gases becomes more rapid until eventually the wood ignites. As soon as the gases burn to form flames the fire spreads rapidly.

Impregnation of timber with certain salts greatly reduces its flammability, and prevents flaming and smouldering after the source of heat is removed. The first salts used for this purpose were strongly hygroscopic ones which had a most unfortunate effect on any paint or varnish that was subsequently applied to the treated wood. The chemicals used also had a corrosive action on metals which led to the failure of fastenings. For some years these disadvantages checked the use of fire retardant chemicals, until improved formulations became available.

Modern treatments to increase the fire resistance of wood are of two types:

1. Impregnation with high concentrations of certain salts which prevent flaming and glowing of the wood after the source of heat has been removed.
2. Surface application of fire retardant coatings or paints which delay ignition and check the spread of flames.

Impregnation Treatments

The methods used for injecting fire retardant chemicals into wood are similar to those used for impregnating timber with preservative salts; the only difference being that higher retentions are required. The full cell process is always employed.

The chemical now most generally used for such treatments is ammonium phosphate, the monammonium and diammonium salts being preferred. The degree of protection afforded depends on the quantity of the salt introduced into the wood. Flame proofing may be achieved with a retention of about 2lbs. of dry salts per cubic ft. of wood, while maximum fire protection is given by a loading of about 5 lbs. of salts per cubic ft. A retention of about 3 lbs. per cubic ft., equivalent to about 8% of the dry weight of the wood, is commonly specified for structural timbers.

Boric acid, which inhibits smouldering even at relatively low concentrations, is often mixed with monammonium phosphate. It has in addition antiseptic properties which prevent fungal and insect attack on the treated wood.

After impregnation treated timber should be redried before use. It is generally more satisfactory to carry out such drying in kilns than to depend on air drying. If the timber is to be used for joinery, shop fittings, or cabin linings in ships, the moisture content should be reduced to 8-10%, which will certainly involve kiln drying. For structural timbers, such as rafters, a moisture content of 14-15% would be suitable.

Surface Treatments

Though timber can be rendered resistant to prolonged heating, or a high temperature, only by thorough impregnation, the rate of spread of flame can be greatly reduced by certain surface treatments. Any covering of a non-combustible material, such as plaster, will prevent ignition of wood; but fire retardant coatings are generally understood to imply a paint, or paste, that can be applied to the surface of the wood by brushing. Such paints can act either by preventing the access to the wood of the oxygen necessary for combustion, or by swelling up to provide an insulating layer. These last are often called intumescent coatings.

Sodium silicate (waterglass) is a common ingredient of many fire resisting paints. This retains its effectiveness better if mixed with an inert filler. A specified composition is:

> Kaolin 150 lbs.
> Sodium silicate (sp. gr. about 1.42) 112 lbs.
> Water 100 lbs.

The application of two coats of this paint, to give a coverage of 20 sq. yds. per gallon in the two coats, is recommended.

A strong solution (about 30%) of ammonium phosphate also gives quite good protection if two or three coats are applied.

Some of the best coatings are of the intumescent type, which are based on a mixture of a urea formaldehyde with ammonium phosphate, together with a filler when an opaque finish is required.

There are many effective fire retardant paints on the market, but these vary considerably in their resistance to the weather, and some are quite unsuitable for external use.

Uses for Fire Retardant Wood

Fire retardants have their greatest value for preventing the outbreak of fire, and for checking its rate of spread in the early stages when every minute counts. In this connection it is worth quoting the opinion of S. H. Clarke, sometime Director of the Fire Research Organisation. He says this: 'When suitably applied treatment may be expected to prevent an outbreak of fire, to delay development in the early stages and to lessen the hazard to means of escape. . . . Fire retardant treatments would therefore appear to be appropriate to fabrics, to light timbers, or to woodwork where even a slight improvement in resistance to fire might be critical, for instance in ships, or the upper storeys of high buildings . . . and in large temporary buildings such as exhibitions, where it is of first importance to ensure the safety of the public'. His final conclusion was that there is a good case for using fire retardant treatments for light timbers in many situations.

Wall boards, especially soft insulating boards, permit very rapid spread of flame, and surface linings of such material should never be left unprotected. Board should be used that has been treated during manufacture with fire retardant chemicals, or, alternatively, the exposed surfaces should be thoroughly treated with an effective fire resistant paint.

The practical applications of flame-proofed timber listed by Salmon (1960) included its use for the construction of flues in coke quenching towers, and for smoke boards under bridges where there are highly corrosive atmospheres as well as high temperatures.

There is no great advantage to be gained from treating large sized structural timbers with fire retardants. The rate of burning of such timbers as large beams and roof trusses is in any case quite slow, and after a fire they will often be found to be charred only on the surface. Wood is a poor conductor of heat, and though the surface of a beam may be burning only a small proportion of the heat is transmitted back into the core which does not, therefore, become hot enough to liberate flammable gases. For this reason large timber beams retain their mechanical strength during conflagration for much longer than unprotected metal ones, which collapse when the metal reaches a critical temperature.

Combined Fire and Rot Proofing Treatments

There are certain situations in which protection against both fire and fungal decay may be required, notably in mines. The 1953 report of the Safety in Mines Research Establishment recorded that:

'Untreated timber, particularly the timber lagging of roadways, provided the main fuel in at least four serious fires during 1953. These fires stress the need for the fire retardant treatment of timber, not only for the lagging of mine roadways and for ventilation doors, but also for surface structures such as the timber supports of winding gear.'

L

Large quantities of pitwood are now being impregnated with fire retardant preservatives in a number of countries. It is a simple matter to include in a mixture of fire retardant chemicals salts that are toxic to fungi, and thus to achieve protection against decay while conferring fire resistance to the wood. Probably boron compounds are the most suitable additions as they themselves contribute to the fire retardant properties of the mixture, effectively inhibiting smouldering of the wood. Boric acid is practically non-hygroscopic and has very little corrosive effect on metals. At the same time it is highly toxic to wood-rotting fungi and insects, even at relatively low concentrations.

CHAPTER XIV

ECONOMIC ASPECTS OF
WOOD PRESERVATION

THE economic advantages that result from preservative treatment of timber in contact with the ground have long been recognised by the railways, postal authorities, and the public utility companies, in all developed and industrialised countries. It is only in comparatively recent times, however, that the value of preservative treatment for mining timbers has been fully appreciated, and it is still not sufficiently recognised by the building industry, and by those who use timber in their farms and gardens for fencing, greenhouses etc.

The annual cost of an item or unit depends on the first cost (in place) divided by the number of years that the item lasts. More precisely, the annual cost may be defined as the annual payment required to extinguish an interest-bearing debt during a period corresponding to the life of the material in service. It can be derived from the following formula:

$$A = P \left(\frac{r(1+r)^n}{(1+r)^n - 1} \right)$$

A is the annual charge
P is the cost of material plus cost of erection
r is the rate of interest expressed as a decimal
n is the estimated service life—obtained if possible from service tests.

To give a simple example (without taking into account the interest charges on the sums involved) let us consider the following case:

If an untreated gate post, value 20/-, costs 20/- to erect, and lasts 10 years, its annual cost will be $\frac{40}{10} = 4/\text{-}$.
A fully impregnated post might cost 25/-, the cost of erection will be the same as for the untreated post, and the life may well extend to 50 years, giving an annual cost of approximately $\frac{45}{50} = 10\frac{1}{2}$d.

Failure of a piece of wood in a building through decay may involve expense enormously greater than the cost of the actual piece of wood itself. If, for instance, the end of a main tie beam in a church roof fails, repairs may cost hundreds of pounds, though the piece of wood itself may only be worth a few pounds, while the cost of adequately pre-treating it might have involved only a few shillings.

Hunt and Garrett quote examples of how replacement charges may far exceed the cost of the structural item itself. For instance the cost of replacing a pole in a high voltage transmission line may be as high as $200, while the delivered price may be only $30-50. Similarly the expense of replacing a set of mining timbers was over $20, though the cost of the timber had been only about $8. Another example they quote was the cost of replacing, after only 6 years, untreated bulkheads in barges which originally cost $220. Omitting altogether the cost of the new material the expense of the work involved was $1500, plus $600 for the loss of service of the barge while undergoing repairs.

Hollingsworth, in his consideration of the economy of preserving mining timber, drew attention to the savings in re-installation costs. He pointed out that it is a very expensive operation to replace track because of decayed sleepers, or supports because of decayed props or cover boards.

Many striking instances of the very heavy expenditure involved in replacing timbers that decayed prematurely owing to lack of preservative treatment have come to the notice of the author. The following may be quoted as typical of many others:

1. A large wharf in North London was erected using 1000 12″ × 12″ Douglas Fir stanchions to support the roof. These were set in concrete bases resting in damp soil. After less than five years the bases of many of the stanchions began to decay where they were in contact with the damp concrete. To preserve the roof against eventual structural collapse (it carried overhead cranes) it was necessary to pick up each stanchion separately, cut off the decayed portions, treat the ends with preservative, and then insert a damp proof course between the base of the post and the concrete. The total cost of the repairs amounted to £8000, which was at least ten times as much as it

would have cost to have given the timbers adequate protection before they were set in position.

2. In a modern hospital in Yorkshire the ceilings over some of the wards were fixed to wooden battens set in concrete beams. These battens had received some fire proofing treatment which did not have any preservative action against fungal attack, but which, by its somewhat hygroscopic nature, tended to keep the wood damp. Within three years of its construction the fastenings into these battens were becoming loose, and the ceiling was pronounced unsafe. It was an extremely awkward and costly job to remove the battens as they had to be dug out piecemeal from the concrete beams in which they were embedded, and the whole ceiling had to be replaced.

3. A flour mill in N. Ireland was constructed near the water's edge on a concrete raft resting on heavy wooden piles which had received no preservative treatment. The earth in which the piles were driven was not all below the permanent water table, and so the upper ends of the poles were not kept sufficiently wet to inhibit fungal decay. After a while they began to crumble and the concrete raft supporting the heavy building with all its machinery cracked, and in places subsided, necessitating most expensive underpinning operations. All this would never have occurred had the piles been properly creosoted under pressure, at an extra cost of, at the most, a few hundred pounds.

These examples show how unwise it is to omit preservation of important structural timbers if there is the slightest chance of their being exposed to persistent dampness in use. It is bad enough to have to replace fence posts at frequent intervals because they have not been properly treated, but the penalties for inadequate protection of important structural timbers are very much more severe.

Salvage Value of Treated Timbers

If a structure has to be replaced because it has become obsolete the salvage value of any well treated timber used in its construction is likely to be higher than that of any of the other materials. Steel, it is true, has some value but the cost of recovering it is high, and concrete has practically no salvage value. Hunt and Garrat quote several instances where creosoted piles have been recovered in perfect condition from old wharfs, after 20-30 years service in waters infested with marine borers, and these have been re-used in new structures.

In this country old creosoted railway sleepers are often used to make fencing and they give many years of useful service as posts or palings. Finally at the end of their service such timbers yield excellent firewood. When the streets of London used to be paved with creosoted blocks there was a ready sale for the old ones as they made such good fuel.

Increased Market for Preserved Timber

There was at one time a marked lack of interest in wood preservation among timber merchants, some of whom took the shortsighted view that the faster the timber rotted the more of it they would sell. While this might have been true hundreds of years ago when there were few alternatives to timber, it is far from being the case to-day. If a wooden structure fails through decay it is more than likely that the designer of its replacement will look for a durable alternative rather than replace it again in wood. This has already happened in many different fields. Steel arches have replaced timber pit props; concrete fence posts have been used in place of wooden ones; fibre glass hulls are becoming popular for small boats. In some cases the substitute material has some other advantage over wood besides the increased durability, but in others it is definitely less desirable. Concrete fence posts, for instance, are very much heavier than wooden ones, and no plastic floor covering has the beauty and wearing quality of the really dense hardwoods.

New markets will have to be found for the greatly increased quantities of thinnings coming from the new plantations of both private owners and the State. Most of this material will consist largely of softwoods containing a high proportion of sapwood. This is by nature of low durability, but can quite cheaply be transformed into highly durable building material by appropriate and adequate preservative treatment.

If wood is to retain many of its traditional markets, and also find new ones, far more must be done to bring to the notice of timber users, and the public generally, the knowledge of the advances that the wood preserving industry has made during the last twenty years. A vigorous effort must be made to bring to the notice of all concerned the fact that wood preservation pays handsome dividends.

REFERENCES

Hunt, G., and Garrett, G. A. *Wood Preservation*, 2nd edition, New York, 1958.

Kollmann, F. *Holz als roh und Werkstoff*, **17** (7), 22, 1959.

PROPRIETARY WOOD PRESERVATIVES

THE following list of preservatives which are generally available in Great Britain is not claimed to be by any means a complete list of all the products that are marketed in this country. The omission of any product should not be taken to imply that it is necessarily in any way inferior to those listed.

The information about the composition of the preservatives and their special uses has kindly been supplied by the manufacturers of the products.

Many preservatives can be used effectively for more than one purpose, but to avoid repetition they are usually listed below only once, either in the group which is indicated by their composition, or for the specific purpose for which they have been formulated.

TAR OILS

TAR OIL PRESERVATIVES FOR PRESSURE IMPREGNATION
Creosote to British Standard Specification 144

FOR SURFACE TREATMENTS
Creosote to British Standard 3051, Coal Tar Oil Types of Wood Preservative (other than Creosote to B.S. 144)

Brunolinum, made by Preservation Developments Ltd. Available in several shades
Solignum, made by Solignum Ltd. Available in several shades

WATER-BORNE PRESERVATIVES

FOR PRESSURE IMPREGNATION

Product	Manufacturer	Principal Ingredients	Comments
Celcure	Celcure Ltd.	Copper sulphate and dichromates. (See BWPA Standard 100)	A well fixed general purpose preservative; leaves timber clean; harmless to animals; widely used in refrigerated ships, cold stores, marine piling
Celcure A	Celcure Ltd.	Similar to above but with addition of arsenic. (See BWPA Standard 102)	More toxic to insects (termites) than Celcure

Product	Manufacturer	Principal Ingredients	Comments
Tanalith U	Hickson's Timber Impregnation Co. Ltd.	Sodium dichromate, sodium arsenate, sodium fluoride and Dinitrophenol. (See BWPA Standard 101)	A clean preservative toxic to fungi, insects (termites). Treated wood may be glued and painted
Tanalith C	Hickson's Timber Impregnation Co. Ltd.	Potassium dichromate, copper sulphate and arsenic pentoxide. (See BWPA Standard 103)	An all purpose preservative, that becomes completely fixed in the wood. Non-staining; may be painted over
Timbor	Borax Consolidated Ltd.	Borax-Boric acid	Toxic to fungi and insects but non-poisonous to animals

For Diffusion Treatments

Product	Manufacturer	Principal Ingredients	Comments
Cobra Salts	Cobra (Wood Treatment) Ltd.	Dinitrophenol, sodium fluoride and arsenious anhydride	Primarily intended for treatment of poles
Timbor	Borax Consolidated Ltd.	Borax-Boric acid	See previous table
Woodtreat	Preservation Developments Ltd.	Pentachlorophenol	Claimed to give deep penetration. Specially useful for large-sized timbers

For Surface Treatment

Product	Manufacturer	Principal Ingredients	Comments
Pestcure	George E. Gray	Sodium pentachloro-phenate and dieldrin	Used both in pre-treatment and eradication work
Wolmanol	Hickson's Timber Impregnation Co. Ltd.		Highly concentrated preservative used for in-situ dry rot repair work

SOLVENT TYPE PRESERVATIVES
For Surface Application

Product	Manufacturer	Principal Ingredients	Comments
Brunophen	Preservation Developments Ltd.	Pentachlorophenol and dieldrin	Protection against decay and insect attack
Cuprinol Wood Preserver, Green	Cuprinol Ltd.	Copper naphthenate	Protects against insect attack and decay. Particularly suitable for horticultural timbers

Solvent Type Preservatives for Surface Application (*Contd.*)

Product	Manufacturer	Principal Ingredients	Comments
Cuprinol Wood Preserver, Clear	Cuprinol Ltd.	Zinc naphthenate and other preservatives	Protects against decay and insect attack
Dipsan	Richardson and Starling Ltd.	Chloronaphthalenes and phenol and tin compounds in a volatile solvent	Particularly for new joinery
Impratox	Cobra (Wood Treatments) Ltd.	Pentachlorophenol	Protects against decay and insect attack
Protim Brown	Gallwey Chemical Co. Ltd.	Pentachlorophenol, copper compounds. Chloronaphthalenes plus chlorinated insecticides	For pre-treatment
Protim Clear Green	Gallwey Chemical Co. Ltd.	Penta. Zinc compounds Chloronaphthalenes, plus chlorinated insecticides	For colourless pre-treatment and eradication work
Rentokil Wood Preservative	Rentokil Ltd.	Penta. and dieldrin plus some chloronaphthalene	Protects against decay and insect attack
Rentokil Wood Preservative, Green	Rentokil Ltd.	Copper naphthenate	Horticultural use
Solignum Water Repellent	Solignum Ltd.		Especially for joinery
Wykamol Plus	Richardson and Starling Ltd.	Benzene hexachloride, polychloronaphthalene o.p.p. and organo-tin compounds in volatile solvent	Non-staining, water resistant
Xylamon Clear	Desowag-Chemie GMBH		Insecticide and fungicide for curative and preventive treatment. Odourless after drying
Xylamon Protective	Desowag-Chemie GMBH		For pre-treatment of timber in bulk, for dipping on site and in timber yards
Xylamon Stay Brown	Desowag-Chemie GMBH	Chloronaphthalene plus a non-fugitive brown dye	For exterior timber where permanent staining effect is desired. Preventative only and effective life of stain is approx. 3 years

INSECTICIDAL PRESERVATIVES FOR ERADICATION WORK

Product	Manufacturer	Principal Ingredient	Comments
Cuprinol Standard Woodworm Killer	Cuprinol Ltd.	Metal naphthenate and chlorinated hydrocarbons	For eradication of woodworm from furniture and other timbers, and to prevent re-infestation
Cuprinol Special Duty Woodworm Killer	Cuprinol Ltd.	as above	For eradication of woodworm from unpolished structural timbers and to prevent re-infestation
Rentokil Woodworm Killer	Rentokil Ltd.	Orthodichlorobenzene, trichloronaphthalene, dieldrin and penta.	For eradication of woodworm and prevention of re-infestation
Wykamol	Richardson and Starling Ltd.	BHC, polychloronaphthalene	Primarily for eradication of insects

SOLUTIONS FOR STERILISATION OF BRICKWORK INFECTED WITH DRY ROT

Product	Manufacturer	Principal Ingredient	Comments
Brunobrite	Preservation Developments Ltd.	Sodium pentachlorophenate	Sold as concentrate to be diluted before use
Cuprinol for Brickwork	Cuprinol Ltd.	Sodium pentachlorophenate	
Protim Wall Solution	Gallwey Chemical Co. Ltd.	Aqueous concentrate of sodium pentachlorophenate plus wetting agent	
Santobrite Solution	Monsanto Chemicals Ltd.	Sodium pentachlorophenate	Sold in bulk by manufacturer
Solignum Anti-Fungi Solution	Solignum Ltd.	Sodium pentachlorophenate	

SOLUTIONS SPECIALLY FORMULATED FOR USES IN BOATS

Product	Manufacturer	Principal Ingredients	Comments
Hultox Liquid Concentrate	Richardson and Starling Ltd.	Sodium orthophenyl- phenate and boron compounds	Is added to water used in swilling down and washing boats and ships. Penetrates cracks and crevices
Hultox Bilge Bags	Richardson and Starling Ltd.		Fungicidal salts con- tained in a canvas bag for fixing in boat hulls to render bilge water toxic to normal forms of decaying fungi
Wykamol Plus Marine	Richardson and Starling Ltd.	Similar to Wykamol Plus (see solvent type) but less volatile solvent	For treatment of tim- ber in boats

PRESERVATIVES FOR HORTICULTURAL USE

Cuprinol Wood Preserver, Green	Cuprinol Ltd.	Copper naphthenate	Harmless to plants once solvent has dried off
Solignum VDK	Solignum Ltd.	Copper naphthenate	Harmless to plants once solvent has dried off
Solignum Horticultural Dep.	Solignum Ltd.		Similar to above but cheaper and intended for seed boxes

PRESERVATIVES FOR LOG PROTECTION

Hexa plus	Preservation Developments Ltd.	Benzene hexachloride	For protection of logs against Ambrosia Beetle
Protoplus	Preservation Developments Ltd.		Similar to above but also contains fungicide giving protection against sapstain

PRESERVATIVES FOR PROTECTION OF SAWN TIMBER

Product	Manufacturer	Principal Ingredients	Comments
Lyxastain	Preservation Developments Ltd.	Benzene hexachloride	To prevent *Lyctus* attack
Santobrite	Monsanto Chemicals Ltd.	Sodium pentachlorophenate	For prevention of sap-stain

FIRE RETARDANT WOOD PRESERVATIVES

Celcure F	Celcure Ltd.	Combination of Celcure with fire retardant salts	Applied as 16-20% sol. to give 2·5 lbs./cub. ft. retention
Pyroleith	Hickson's Timber Impregnation Co. Ltd.	Fire retardant salts combined with Tanalith C	Makes timber less flammable and protects against decay
Pyromors	Desowag-Chemie GMBH		

MISCELLANEOUS PRESERVATIVES FOR SPECIAL PURPOSES

Ceetox	Richardson and Starling Ltd.	Organo-tin compounds and silicone resins	Specially for cedar shingles, non-staining, persistent; kills algae and mosses
Cobra salts	Cobra (Wood Treatment) Ltd.	See above	For spot impregnation of poles
Protim Plugs	Gallwey Chemical Co. Ltd.		For insertion in damp walls infected with dry rot fungus
Protim Joinery Linings	Gallwey Chemical Co. Ltd.		A damp proof course material
Red Cedar Solignum	Solignum Ltd.		
Xylamon Blue Stain Primer	Desowag-Chemie GMBH		'Blued' timber can be treated and subsequently painted without ill effect
Xylamon L.X. Hardening	Desowag-Chemie GMBH		For badly decayed works of art. Toxic to insects and fungi; hardens wood to which it is applied

INDEX